THE MINIATURE SCORE SERIES

FAMOUS INDIVIDUAL SYMPHONIES IN SCORE

Edited and devised by
ALBERT E. WIER

The system of arrow signals and special typographical markings, employed in this work to enable those unacquainted with the art of score reading to follow the instrumental outline and to identify the various themes as they appear and recur, is the subject of a pending application for Letters Patent of the United States owned by Harcourt, Brace and Company, Inc.

BONANZA BOOKS
NEW YORK

*This edition published by Bonanza Books,
a division of Crown Publishers, Inc., by
arrangement with Harcourt, Brace & World, Inc.*

Printed in the U.S.A.

FAMOUS INDIVIDUAL SYMPHONIES IN SCORE

INDEX

PREFACE

For the comprehension of orchestral scores, even with the assistance of the system of arrow signals employed in this volume, ability to read instrumental music in both treble and bass clefs is necessary.

It must also be borne in mind that certain wind instruments, such as the clarinet (except the clarinet in C), the French horn (except the horn in C) and the trumpets (except the trumpet in C) are transposing instruments; also that the parts for several string and wind instruments are written in the Alto and Tenor clefs, therefore some knowledge of transposition and of these clefs will be useful.

Four separate pages of miniature scores are printed on each large page of this volume. The large page is bisected by horizontal and vertical lines, the miniature pages located numerically as follows:

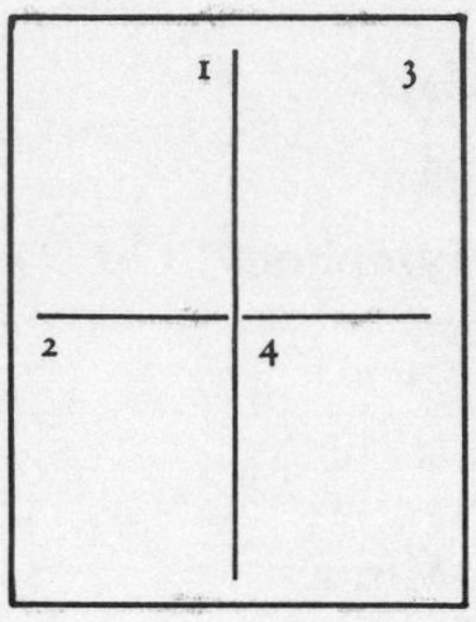

The large pages of this volume are designated by numbers in parentheses at the bottom of the pages; the miniature score pages of each excerpt are numbered separately in the upper right and left hand corners.

Turning to Page 148, containing the first four pages in miniature of the score of Symphony No. 7 by Anton Bruckner, it will be noted that Page 1 (on the miniature page) contains nine bars of music with a separate line provided for each instrument, the name being noted before the line. On Page 2 of the miniature score it will be noted that two sections of scoring are given—each comprising several measures. This is known as score condensation, that is, all instruments that have no notes to play during the eight measures of the first section on the page are omitted, and all instruments that have no notes to play in the eight measures of the second section are omitted. The presence of two or more sections of scoring on one page is always indicated by the mark **//** between each section, and this mark must be carefully observed when reading score.

The system of arrow signals used in this volume will be easily comprehended if its purpose is fully understood before attempting to make use of them. The purpose, starting with the first measure of each excerpt, is to indicate the main melodic line as it progresses from instrument to instrument in the wood-wind, brass, string, and percussion sections of the orchestra. A practical example of this method of score reading is given on the opposite page.

EXPLANATION OF ARROW SIGNAL SYSTEM

The pages used here for explanatory purposes are the first two pages of the Symphony No. 7 by Anton Bruckner. (Complete score on Pages 148-189).

The circled numbers near the arrows are used *only on these pages to aid* in clarifying the explanation; they are *not used* elsewhere in the volume.

Arrow No. 1 indicates the beginning of a tremolo accompaniment figure in the 1st and 2nd violins.

Arrows Nos. 2 & 3 indicate the first announcement of the principal theme in the French horn and violoncellos.

Arrow No. 4 indicates the addition of the violas in announcing the principal theme.

Arrows Nos. 5 & 6 indicate the continuance of the principal theme in the violas and violoncellos.

Arrow No. 7 indicates the addition of the 1st clarinet to the melodic line.

The mark // indicates the separation of Page 2 into two sections of scoring.

Arrows Nos. 8 & 10 indicate the continuance of the melodic line in the 1st clarinet and violoncellos.

Arrow No. 9 indicates the continuance of the tremolo accompaniment figure in the 1st and 2nd violins.

Arrows Nos. 11 & 12 indicate the repetition of the principal theme in the flutes and violins.

MOVEMENTS:

I. *Largo-Allegro Agitato (Reveries and Passions)*

II. *Valse Allegro non troppo (A Ball)*

III. *Adagio (Country Scenes)*

IV. *Allegretto non troppo (March to the Scaffold)*

V. *Larghetto-Allegro assai (Witch's Sabbath)*

The "Fantastic" Symphony is scored for the following instruments:

1 Flauto Piccolo (Piccolo)	*Picc.*	2 Tuben (Tubas)	*Tb.*
2 Flauti (Flutes)	*Fl.*	4 Timpani (Tympani)	*Timp.*
2 Oboi (Oboes)	*Ob.*	Piatti (Cymbals)	*Ptti.*
2 Clarinetti (Clarinets)	*Clar.*	Gran Cassa (Bass Drum)	*G. C.*
1 Corno inglese (English Horn)	*Cor. ingl.*	2 Arpi (Harps)	*Arp.*
2 Fagotti (Bassoons)	*Fag.*	1. Violini (1st Violins)	*Viol.*
4 Corni (Horns)	*Cor.*	2. Violini (2nd Violins)	*Viol.*
2 Cornetti à pistons (Cornets)	*C. à p.*	Violi (Violas)	*Vla.*
2 Trombe (Trumpets)	*Tr.*	Violoncelli (Violoncellos)	*Vc.*
3 Tromboni (Trombones)	*Tbni.*	Contrabassi (Double Basses)	*Cb.*

Each instrument is listed above under its name as printed on the first page of the score; its English equivalent, and the abbreviation used on succeeding pages.

The "Fantastic" Symphony was completed by Berlioz in 1830, and performed for the first time in December of the same year. There is no accurate record of its first performance in the United States.

According to the composer, the program underlying the symphony is as follows: in the first movement a lover meets the lady of his dreams; in the second movement he attends a ball; in the third, for some unexplained reason, he marches to his death on the gallows after killing his love and attempting suicide; in the last movement he sees the witches dancing around his coffin after they have held a burlesque of the burial services in which the *Dies Irae* and the diabolical theme of the dance are intermingled. A slow, dreamy motive, intended to symbolize the idea of perfect love, is presented in the first movement and recurs in the other four.

Critical opinion was greatly divided when the symphony was first heard; it created a veritable sensation, and was both attacked and defended with the greatest violence. Today it is regarded by authorities as a marvelously audacious work, so revolutionary in its orchestration that Liszt, Meyerbeer, Wagner, Strauss and all the great Russian composers found it a source of both inspiration and instruction.

There are two excellent recordings of the "Fantastic" Symphony: One by the Paris Symphony Orchestra with Pierre Monteux; the second by the London Symphony Orchestra with Felix Weingartner.

Fantastic Symphony

Träumereien. Leidenschaften — Reveries. Passions

INTRODUCTION

Largo M.M. ♩ = 56. — Hector Berlioz, Op. 14

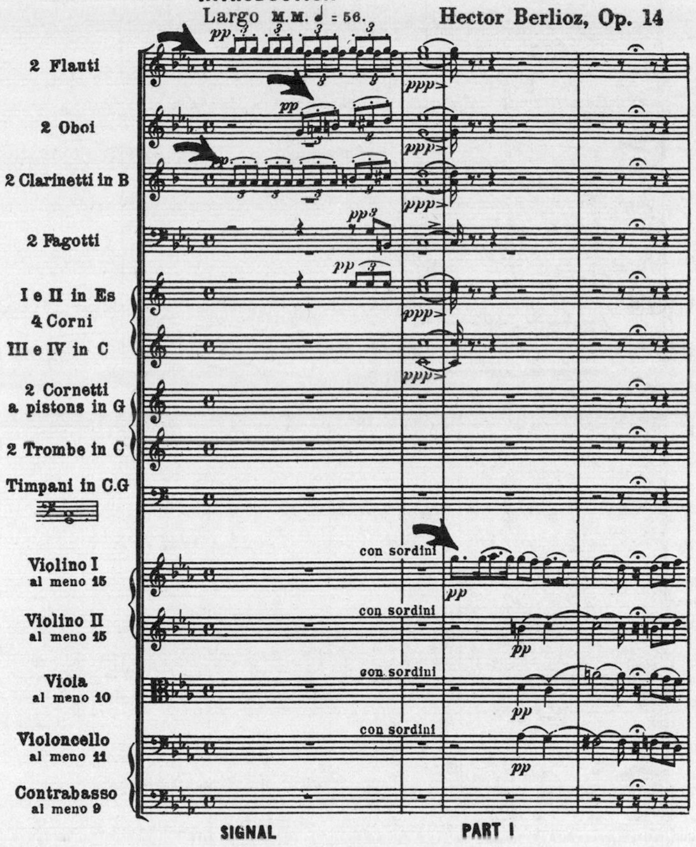

5
Tempo I
un poco ritard.
p dolce
Fl.
Ob.
Cl.
a 2
dolce
Fg.
(Es)
Cor.
(C)
Vl.
poco ritard.
p > pp
arco cresc. molto
Vla.
pizz.
Vc.
arco
cresc. molto
poco ritard.
Cb.
PART 5
I.

6
Fl.
Clar.
Fag.
Cor.
Viol.
Vla.
Vc.
Cb.
cresc.
unis

7
Fl.
Ob.
Cl.
Fg.
(Es)
Cor.
(C)
Vl.
Vla.
Vc.
Cb.
PART 6
I. Solo

8
non rall.
Solo
Fl.
Ob.
Clar.
Fag.
Viol
pizz.
arco
Vla.
Vc.
Cb
PART 7
Cor. I. Solo
con sord. arco
ppp leggiero

10

Allegro agitato e appassionato assai. M.M. 𝅗𝅥 = 132.

PART 8—BRIDGE PASSAGE

12 **EXPOSITION**

13
Fl.
Vla.
Vc.e Cb.
a tempo
Vl.
un poco rit.
a tempo con fuoco
Vc.
Cb.

15
Fl.
Ob.
Cl.
Fg.
(Es) Cor. (C)
C.à.p. (G)
Tr. (C)
Timp.
Vl.
Vla.
Vc.
Cb.
arco

14
un poco rit.
un poco animando
FIRST SUBORDINATE THEME

16
Fl.
Ob.
Cl.
Fag.
Cor.
C.à.p.
Tr.
Timp.
Viol.
Vla.
Vc
Cb

17
Fl.
Ob.
Cl.
Fg.
Es
Cor.
(C)
C.a.p.
(G)
Tr.
(C)
Timp.
Vl.
Vla.
Vc.
Cb.
div.
unis.
pizz.

18
Fl.
Ob.
Cl.
Fag.
Cor.
C. a. p.
Tr.
Timp.
Viol.
Vla.
Vc.
Cb.
Solo.
dolce
cresc.
arco

19
Fl.
Ob.
Cl.
Fg.
(Es)
Cor.
(C)
C.a.p.
(G)
Tr.
(C)
Timp.
Vl.
Vla.
Vc.
Cb.
Solo.
SECOND SUBORDINATE THEME

20
Fl.
Ob.
Cl.
Fag.
Cor.
Cap.
Tr.
Timp.
Viol.
Vla.
Vc.
Cb.
cresc.

DEVELOPMENT
21
Fl.
Ob.
Cl.
Fg.
(Es)
Cor.
(C)
C. à p.
(G)
Tr.
(C)
Timp.
Vl.
Vla.
Vc.
Cb.
pizz.
DEVELOPMENT—SECTION I

22
Fl.
Ob.
Clar.
Fag.
Cor.
Viol.
Vla.
Vc.
Cb.
unis.
cresc.

23
Fl.
Ob.
Cl.
Fg.
(Es)
Cor.
(C)
Timp.
Vl.
Vla.
Vc.
Cb.
a 2.
unis.
DEVELOPMENT—SECTION 2
sempre stacc.
cresc.
decresc.

24
Fl.
Ob.
Cl.
Fag.
Cor.
C. à. p.
Tr.
Timp.
Viol.
Vla.
Vc.
Cb.
a 2.
cresc.
decr.

25

27

RETURNING PASSAGE (RETRANSITION)

26

RECAPITULATION

28

RETURN PRINCIPAL THEME (IDEE FIXE) PART I

RETURN PRINCIPAL THEME (IDEE FIXE) PART II

cresc. e poco pressante.
Fl.
Cl.
Fg.
(Es)
Cor.
(C)
I.
III.
Vl.
Vla.
Vc.
Cb.
RETURN PRINCIPAL THEME (IDEE
FIXE) PART III

Fl
Ob
I.
Cl.
Fag.
Cor.
C.à.p
Tr.
Timp.
Viol.
Vla. div.
Vc.
Cb.

Fl.
Ob.
Cl.
Fg.
(Es)
Cor.
(C)
II.
III.
Cà.p.
(G)
Tr.
(C)
Timp.
Vl.
div.
Vla.
Vc.
Cb.

Fl.
Ob.
I. Solo.
Clar.
Fag.
unis.
cresc. poco a poco
Viol.
Vla.
Vc.
Cb.
cresc. molto

33

Fl.
Ob.
Cl.
Fg.
Vl.
Vla.
Vc.
Cb.
cresc.
molto

34

Fl.
Ob.
Clar.
Fag.
Corni.
Cornet.
Tromp.
Timp.
Viol
Vla
Vc.
Cb.

35

Fl.
Ob.
Cl.
Fg.
(Es)
Cor.
(C)
C.a.p.
(G)
Tr.
(C)
Timp.
Vl.
Vla.
Soli.
Vc.
Cb.
RETURN SECOND SUBORDINATE THEME

36

Fl.
Ob.
Cl.
Fag.
Cor.
C.a.p.
Tr.
Timp.
Viol.
Vla
Vc.
Cb.
cresc.

37
Solo.
Fl.
Ob.
Cl.
Fg.
(Es) Cor. (C)
C.a.p. (G)
Tr. (C)
baguettes d'éponge.
Solo.
Timp.
Vl.
Vla.
Vc.
Cb.
RETURN FIRST SUBORDINATE THEME

38
Clar.
Timp.
div.
Viol
Vla
Vc.
Cb.
un poco riten.
riten.
Fag.
unis.
canto Solo.
poco f
div.
unis.
canto

39
rallent. poco
riten.
Tempo I.
1. Solo. espressivo
Ob.
Cl.
Fg.
Vl.
Vla.
Vc.
Soli.
Cb.
pizz.
SPECIAL THEME
Soli.
div.

40
Ob.
Clar.
cresc.
Fag.
Viol
Vla.
Vc.
unis.
Cb.
arco
Fl
I.
dim.

41
Fl.
Ob.
Cl.
Fg.
Vl.
Vla.
Vc.
Cb.
cresc.
p cresc.
dim.
poco f
p dim.
43
Fl.p.
Fl.II
Ob.
Cl.
Fg.
(Es)
Cor.
(C)
III.
C.à p.
(G)
Tr.
(C)
Timp.
Vl.
Vla.
Vc.
Cb.
f
42
Fl.
Cl.
Fag.
Vl.
Vla.
Vc.
Cb.
p dim.
cresc.
Fl.I.
Fl.II.
Fl.picc.
Ob.
Clar.
Fag. unis.
Cornetti in G.
Viol.
Vla.
Cb.
cresc. molto
44
Fl.p.
Ob.
Cl.
Fag.
Cor.
a 2. C. à p.
Tr.
Timp.
Viol.I. div.
Viol.II. div.
Vla.
div.
unis.
V-celli. div.
non div.
Cb.
ff

45

Fl.p.
Fl.II
Ob.
Cl.
Fg.
(Es)
Cor.
(C)
C.a.p.
(G)
Tr.
(C)
Timp.
Vl.
Vla.
Vc.
div.
Cb.

47

Fl.p.
Fl.II
Ob.
a 2.
Cl.
Fg.
(Es)
Cor.
(C)
C.à.p.
(G)
Tr.
(C)
Timp.
Vl.I
div.
Vl.II
div.
div.
Vla.
unis.
Vc.
Cb.

46

Fl.p.
Fl. II.
Ob.
a 2.
Cl.
Fag.
Cor.
C.à.p.
Tr.
Timp.
baguettes d'éponge.
Vl.
Vla.
Vc.
Cb.

48

Fl. p.
Fl. II.
Ob.
Cl.
Fg.
Cor.
C.à.p.
Tr.
Timp.
Vl. I
Vl. II
Vla.
Vc.

49
animato.
Fl.p.
Fl.II
Ob.
unis.
Cl.
Fg.
cresc.
(Es)
Cor.
(C)
C.à.p.
(G)
Tr.
(C)
Timp.
Vl.
div.
mf
Vla.
Vc.
Cb.
mf pizz.

CODA
51
Tempo I. più animato.
Fl.p.
Fl.II
Ob.
a 2.
Cl.
unis.
Fg.
(Es)
Cor.
(C)
C.à.p.
(G)
Tr.
(C)
Timp.
Vl.
divisi
cresc.
Vla.
Vc.
Cb.
pizz.
CODA—SECTION I

50
ritenuto rallent. poco a poco
Fl.p.
Fl.II.
Solo.
Ob.
Cl.
Fg.
Cor.
C.à.p.
Tr.
Timp. Baguettes d'éponge
Vl.
Vla.
Vc.
Cb.
arco
RETURN PRINCIPAL THEME (IDEE FIXE) PART I

52
Fl.p.
Fl.II
Ob.
Cl.
a 2.
Fg.
Cor.
C.à.p.
Tr.
Timp.
Vl.
unis.
div.
Vla.
Vc.
Cb.
arco

53
Fl.p.
Fl.II
Ob.
Cl.
Fg.
unis.
(Es)
Cor.
(C)
Cà.p.
(G)
Tr.
(C)
Timp.
Vl.
cresc.
Vla.
Vc.
Cb.
CODA—SECTION 2

55
dando e diminuendo poco a poco
un poco
Ob.
Vl.
pizz.
Vla.
pizz.
Vc.
pizz.
Cb.
piu lento
Religiosamente
Fl.
Ob.
Cl.
Fg.
(Es)
Cor.
(C)
Baguettes d'éponge
Timp.
Vl.
arco
divisi
Vla.
arco
Vc.
arco
Cb.
CODA—SECTION 3 (IDEE FIXE)

54
ritar -
Fl. p.
Fl. II.
Ob.
Solo.
Cl.
Fg.
Cor.
C.à.p.
Tr.
Timp.
Vl.
pizz.
arco
arco
pizz.
Vla.
pizz.
arco
arco
Vc.
pizz.
Cb.

56
Fl p.
Fl. II.
Ob.
Cl.
Fg.
Cor.
C.a.p.
Tr.
Timp.
Vl.
Vc.
non div.
Cb

57

Un bal

Ein Ball — A Ball

INTRODUCTION

Valse Allegro non troppo M.M. ♩.=60

59

58

60

Fl.
Ob.
Cl.
(E)
Cor.
(C)
A. I
A. II
dolce e tenero
Vl.
Vla.
Vc.
Cb.
PRINCIPAL THEME

62

rallent.
Viol.
Vla.
Vc.
Cb.
a tempo
Solo.
Arp. I.
Viol.
Vla.
Vc.
pizz.
Cb.
pizz.

Fl.
Ob.
Cl.
(E)
Cor.
(C)
A. I
A. II
Vl.
Vla.
Vc.
Cb.

64

Fl.
p cresc.
Ob.
Cl.
p cresc.
Cor.
A. I
A. II
Vl.
Vla.
Vc.
arco
C.B.
arco

65

66

67

68

FIRST REPETITION—PRINCIPAL THEME

SUBORDINATE THEME (IDEE FIXE)

73

75

74

SECOND REPETITION—PRINCIPAL THEME

76

77

Fl.
Ob.
Cl.
(E)
Cor.
(C)
A. I
A. II
Vl.
Vla.
Vc.
Cb.
p cresc.
f
mf
poco f
pizz.
p

78

Fl.
Ob.
Cl.
Cor.
A. I
A. II
Vla.
V-celli unis.
C-B.
p cresc.
f
arco
p

79

Fl.
Ob.
Cl.
(E)
Cor.
(C)
A. I
A. II
Vl.
Vla.
Vc.
Cb.
f
p
sf
pizz.
mf
arco

80

Fl.
Ob.
Clar.
Viol.
Vla.
Vc.
Cb.
Cor. I. II.
Arp. II.
p
cresc. poco
arco
dim.
div.
pp
poco f > p
cresc.
poco - a - poco - cresc. molto
f
pizz.

81
Fl.
Ob.
Cl.
Cor. (E)
A.I
Vl.
pizz.
arco
Vla.
Vc.
Cb.
Fl. I.
Picc.
unis.
Cor. (E) (C)
Vo. e Cb.

82
rall.
Fl.
Ob.
Clar.
Cor.
cresc.
Arpa I.
Arpa II.
Viol.
Viola.
Vc.
Cb.
arco

83
Tempo I.
rall.
Fl.
Ob.
Cl.
a 2.
(E) Cor. (C)
cresc.
A. I
A. II
Vl.
Vla.
Vc.
Cb.

84
Tempo I.
animato
Fl.
Fl. picc.
Ob.
Cl.
a 2.
Cor.
A. I
A. II
Vl.
Vla.
Vc.
Cb.
cresc. poco

85

Fl.
Fl.p.
Ob.
Cl.
(E)
Cor.
(C)
A.I
A.II
Vl.
Vla.
Vc.
Cb.
cresc.
a poco
cresc. molto
ff

87

a 2.
Fl.
Ob.
Cl.
(E)
Cor.
(C)
A.I
A.II
Vl.
Vla.
Vc.
Cb.
cresc.
p
cresc. poco a poco

86

Fl.
Ob.
Cl.
Cor.
A. I.
A. II.
Vl.
Vla.
Vc.
Cb.
p
mf
pp

88

Fl.
Ob.
Cl.
Cor.
A. I.
A. II.
Vl.
Vla.
Vc.
Cb.
f

89
a 2.
Fl.
Ob.
Cl.
(E)
Cor.
(C)
A. I
A. II
Vl.
Vla.
Vo.
Cb.
ff

90
Fl.
Ob.
Cl.
Cor.
A. I
A. II
Vl.
Vla.
Vc.
Cb.

91
Fl.
Ob.
Cl.
(E)
Cor.
(C)
A. I
A. II
Vl.
Vla.
Vo.
Cb.
ff

92
poco riten.
Fl.
Ob.
Cl.
Solo.
pp
rf
Cor.
Soli.
A. I
A. II
Vl.
Vla.
Vc.
Cb.
p
RETURN SUBORDINATE THEME (IDÉE FIXE)

CODA
93
poco rallent.
rallent.
Tempo I.
con fuoco
Fl.
Ob.
Cl.
(E) Cor. (C)
A. I
A. II
Vl.
Vla.
Vc.
Cb.
95
animato
cresc.
94
96
a 2.
cresc. molto

97

98

99

100

Scène aux champs.
Szene auf dem Lande.— Scenes in the Country.
INTRODUCTION

101
102
103
104
Ob.
C.i.
Vl.
Vla.
Vc.
Cb.
Fl.
Cl.
Cor. (F)
Cor. ingl.
Ob. II.
Viol.
Vla.
Ob.I.
Ob.II.
Fag.
Cor.I.II.
Cor.III.
Cor.IV.
Timp. I.
Timp. II.
Solo
Soli.
perdendo
rinf
senza sord.
non div.
pizz.
arco
dim.
cresc. poco a poco
leggiero
unis.
nella orchestra
rit.
divisi
PRINCIPAL THEME—PART I
PRINCIPAL THEME—PART II
SUBORDINATE THEME

105
a tempo
Fl.
Ob.
Cl.
Fg.
(F)
Cor.
(Es)
(C)
Timp.
Vl.
Vla.
Vc.
Cb.
cresc.
pizz.

106
Fl.
Ob. I e II.
Cl.
Fag.
Cor.
Timp.
Vl.
Vla.
Vc.
Cb.
cresc.
arco

107
Fl.
Ob.
Cl.
Fg.
(F)
Cor.
(Es)
(C)
Timp.
Vl.
Vla.
Vc.
Cb.
cresc.
unis.
pizz.
arco

108
Fl.
Ob.
Cl.
Fag.
Cor. IV.
Viol.
Vla.
Vc.
Cb.
cresc.
dim.
Solo.

Fl.
Ob.
Cl.
Fg.
Cor. (Es)
Vl.
Vla.
Vc.
Cb.
unis.
III.
pizz.
arco
Soli. arco
RETURN PRINCIPAL THEME—PART I

Fl.
Ob.
Cl.
Fg.
(F)
Cor. (Es)
(C)
Timp.
Vl.
Vla.
Vc.
Cb.
Solo
cresc. molto
arco
pizz.

Fl.
Ob.
Cl.
Fag.
Cor. I e II.
Cor. III.
Cor. IV.
Timp. I.
Timp. II.
Viol.
Vla.
Vc.
Cb.

Fl.
Ob.
Cl.
Viol.
Viole unis.
Vc.
Cb.
arco
cresc. poco a
Fag.
Cor. I e II.
Cor. III.
Cor. IV.
Vla.
cresc.
poco
cresc. molto

Fl.
Ob.
Cl.
Fg.
Cor.
(F)
(Es)
(C)
Vl.
Vla.
Vc.
Cb.
Solo.
unis.
dim.
poco a poco
f trem.
espressivo
cresc.
IDÉE FIXE (FROM FIRST MOVEMENT)

Fl.
Ob.
Fg.
Vl.
Vla.
Vc.
Cb.
Cl.
Cor.
(F)
(Es)
(C)
Timp.
animando un poco
cresc.
baguettes de bois.
unis.

Fl.
Ob.
Cl.
Fag.
Vl.
Vla.
Vc.
Cb.
Viol.
animando un poco

Fl.
Ob.
Cl.
Fag.
Vl.
Vl. II.
Vla.
Vc.
Cb.
Cor. IV.
rallent.
dim.
p morendo
pp
Soli.
Tempo I.
pizz.
sempre pizz.
ppp

117
Solo.
pp
Fl.
dolce
mf
Cl.
Vl.
encora più
Vla.
encora più
pizz.
Vc.
pizz.
Cb.
Fl.
Echo.
pppp
Cl.
poco
f
cresc.
ppp
Vl.
pppp
cresc. un poco
Vla.
pppp
cresc. un poco
arco
Vc.
div.
pizz.
p
pizz.
Cb.
p

118
Fl.
p
cresc.
Ob.
Cl. I.
sf
cresc.
sf
decresc.
Cor. I. II.
Cor. III.
cresc.
Viol.
poco
pp
pizz.
Vla.
pizz.
arco
Vc.
poco
pizz.
Cb.
arco
sempre pizz.
cresc.
Fl.
mf
Ob.
Fag.
arco
p
Vcl. unis. non div.
Cb.

119
Fl.
p dolce
Ob.
p
Cl.
p
Fg.
p
Cor. (C)
IV.
p dolce
Vl.
Vla.
Vc.
Cb.
Fl.
Ob.
Cl.
Fg.
Cor. (C)
Vl.
Vla.
Vc.
Cb.

120
Fl.
quasi niente
I.
pppp
Ob.
quasi niente
Cl.
quasi niente
Fag.
quasi niente
Cor. I. II.
Cor. III.
Cor. IV.
Timp.
quasi niente
Viol.
quasi niente
pppp
Vla.
quasi niente
Vc.
quasi niente
Cb.
quasi niente
pppp

121
Fl.
Ob.
Cl.
Fg.
(F)
Cor. (Es)
(C)
Timp.
Vl.
cresc. poco a poco
Vla.
Vc.
Cb.

122
Fl.
Ob.
Cl.
Fag.
Cor.
Timp.
Vl.
cresc.
cresc. molto
Viole div.
Vc.
Cb.

123
Fl.
Ob.
Cl.
Fg.
(F)
Cor. Es
(C)
in F.
Timp.
div.
ff dim. ppp
Vl.
poco
Vla.
Vc.
Cb.

124
Fl.
Solo
Ob.
Cl.
Solo. I.
Fag.
Cor. I in F.
Cor. II in F.
Cor. III in F.
Cor. IV in C.
Timp.
rall.
a tempo
Vl.
Vla.
Vc.
Cb.

125
Fl.
Ob.
Solo.
Cl.
Fg.
Cor.
Timp.
Vl.
p cresc.
Vla.
Vc.
pizz.
Cb.

126
Fl.
Solo.
p legg.
Cl.
Fag.
Timp. II.
baguettes d'éponge.
poco f
dim.
Viol.
Viole div.
poco
Vc.
arco
Cb.
Solo. II
Cor. I. II.
cresc.
Vla.
Solo.
p cresc.

127
perdendo
Fl.
dim.
Ob.
a 2.
Cl.
Fg.
uns.
Cor.
Timp.
Vl.
Vla.
unis.
Vc.
Cb.

128
Fl.
Solo.
sempre
Ob.
Oboe II = Corno inglese.
Cl.
Fag.
Cor. I. II.
Timp.
Vl.
Vla.
div.
Vc.
Cb.

Marche au supplice

Der Gang zum Richtplatz | March to the Gallows

INTRODUCTION

Allegretto non troppo M. M. 𝅗𝅥=72

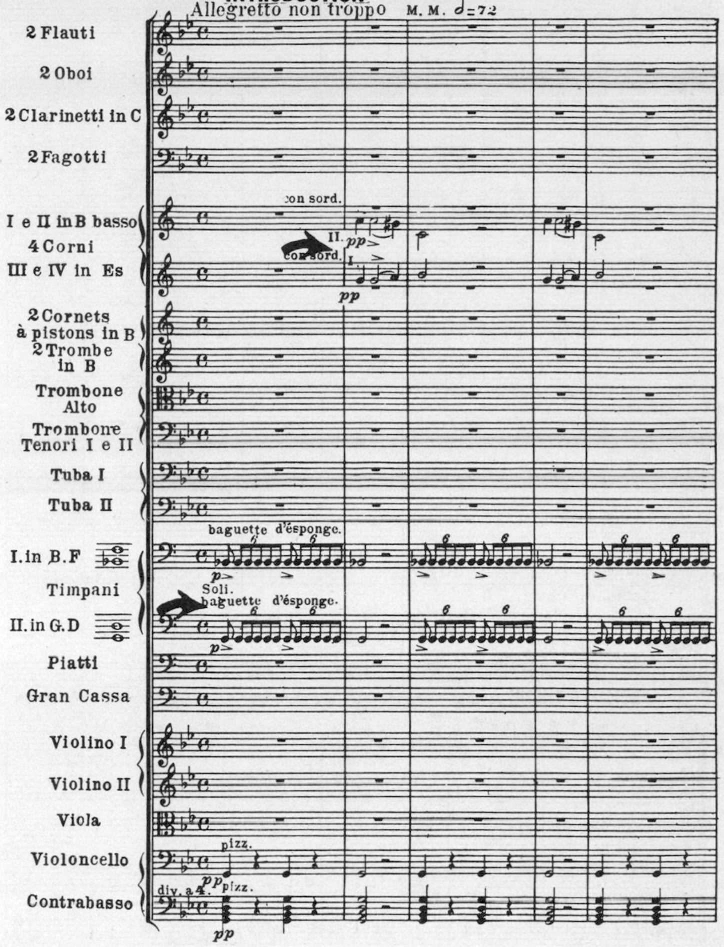

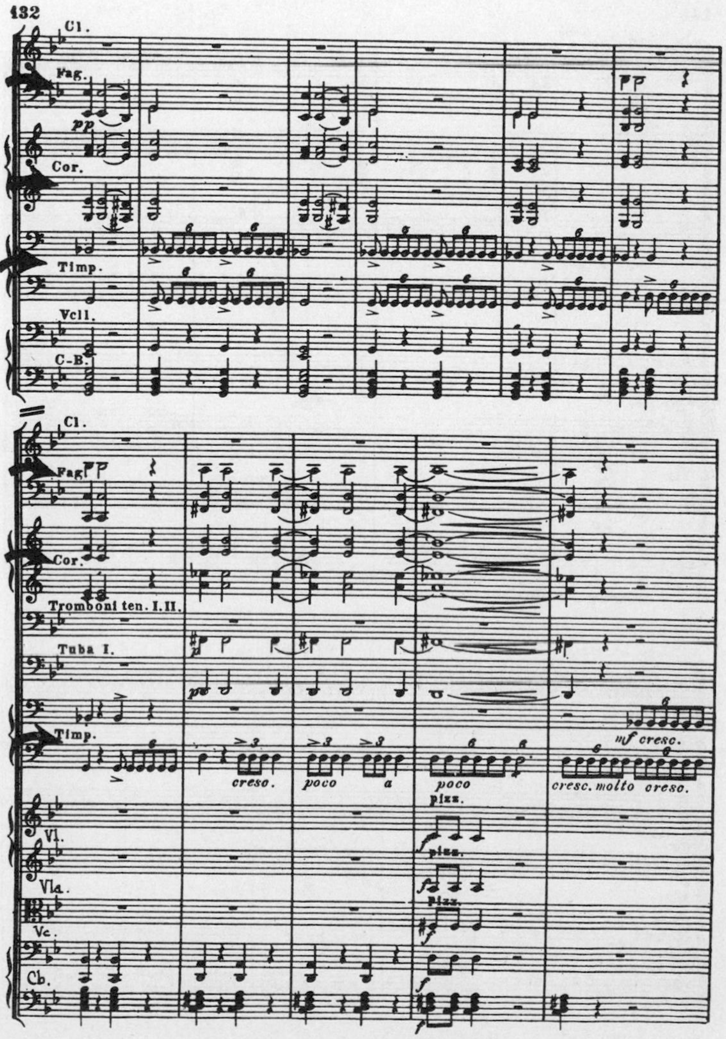

133
135
134
136
PRINCIPAL THEME
Cl.
Fg.
(B) Cor. (Es)
C.à p. (B)
Tr. (B)
Tbni.
Tb.
Timp.
Vl.
Vla.
Vc.
Cb.
Vc. e Cb.
Fl.
Ob.
Ptti.
G. C.
Cor. III. IV.
Viol.
Soli.
unis.
arco
pizz.
dim.
cresc.

SUBORDINATE THEME

DEVELOPMENT

DEVELOPMENT—SECTION

141
Fl.
Ob.
Cl.
Fg.
(B) Cor. Es)
C.à.p. (B)
Tr. (B)
Tbni.
Tb.
Timp.
Ptti.
G.C.
Vl.
Vla.
Vc.
Cb.
Soli.
Solo
pizz.
arco

142
Fl.
Cl.
Fag. unis.
Cor.
C.à.p.
Tr.
Tbni.
Tb.
Timp.
Solo.
poco f
cresc.
Ptti.
G.C.
arco
pizz.
Vla.
Vc.
Cb.

143
Fl.
Ob.
Cl.
Fg.
(B) Cor. (Es)
C.à.p. (B)
Tr. (B)
Tbni.
Tb.
Timp.
Ptti.
G.C.
arco
cresc.
Vl.
Vla.
Vc.
Cb.

144
Fl.
Ob.
Cl.
Fag.
Cor.
C.à.p.
Tbni.
Tb.
Timp.
Ptti.
G.C.
Vl.
Vla.
Vc.
Cb.

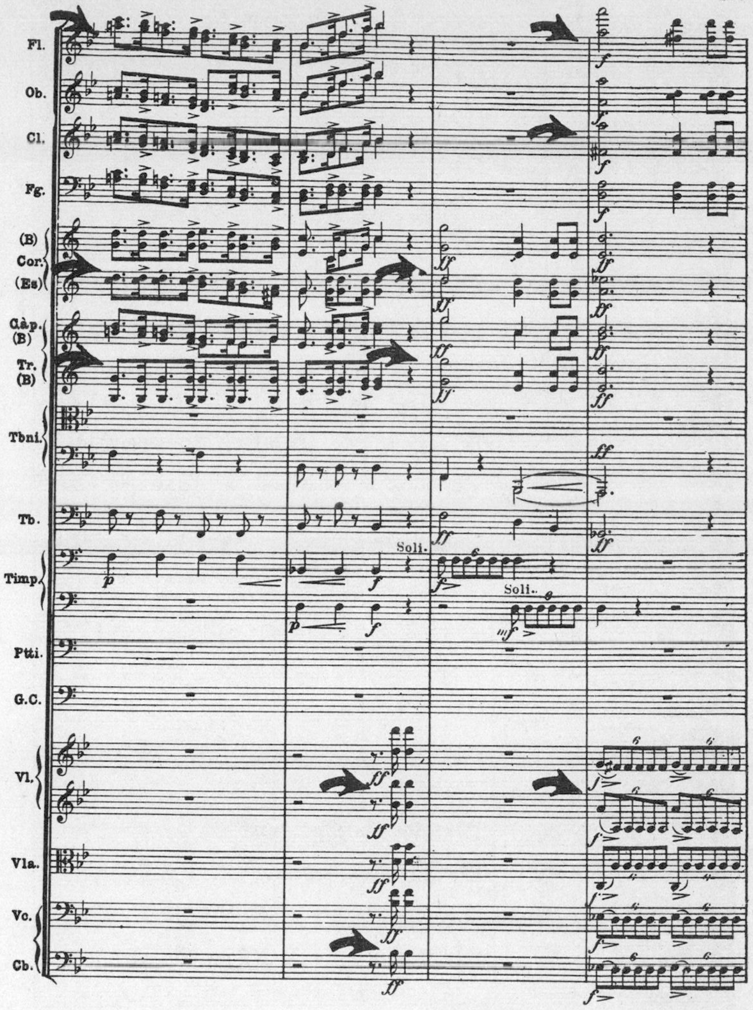

RETURNING PASSAGE (RETRANSITION)

149

150

RECA-

RETURN

PITULATION

151

PRINCIPAL THEME

152

CODA

CODA—SECTION I

CODA—SECTION 2

CODA—SECTION 3 (IDEE FIXE) CODA—SECTION 4

Songe d'une nuit du Sabbat.

Beim Hexen-Sabbath. Dream of a Witches' Sabbath.

Larghetto. M.M. 𝅗𝅥=63. **INTRODUCTION**

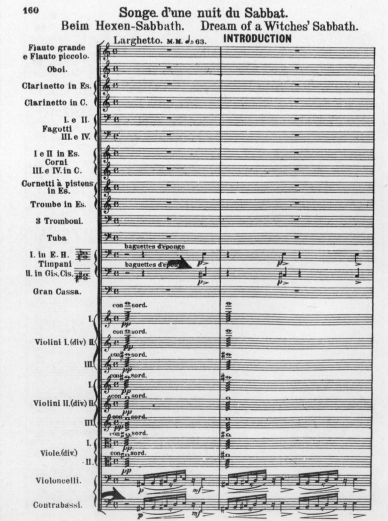

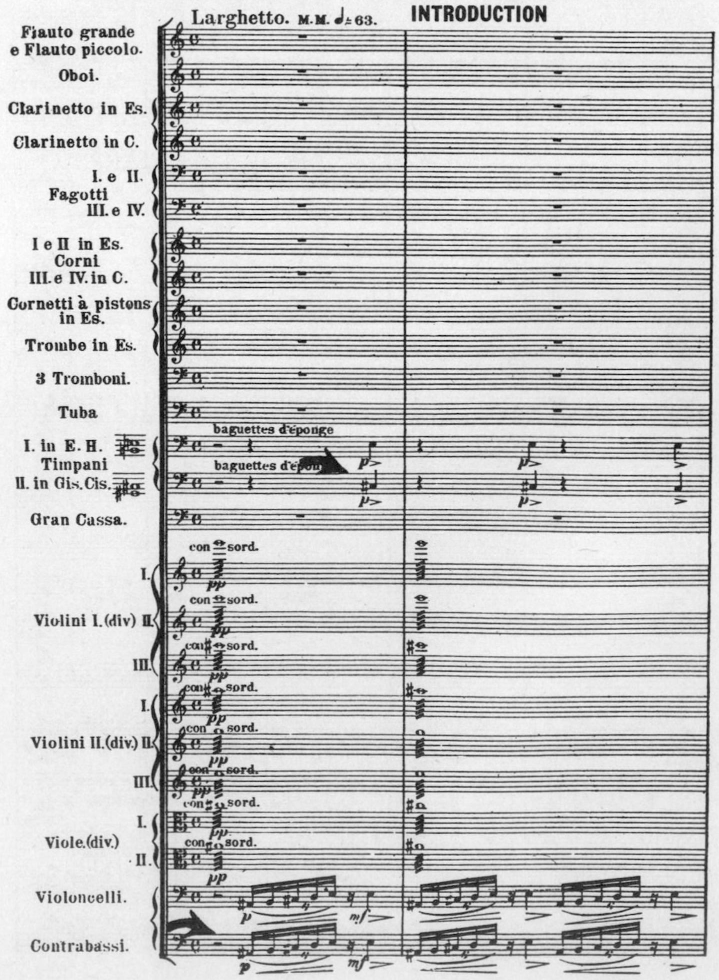

Fl.
Ob.
poco f>p
(Es) Cl. (C)
Fg.
(Es) Cor. (C)
C.à p. (Es)
Tr. (Es)
Tbni.
Tb.
Timp.
muta Cis in C.
G. C.
ppp
Vl. I
Vl. II
Vla.
Vc.
Cb.

a 2.
Soli.
Fl.
Ob.
dim.
(Es) Cl. (C)
Fg.
(Es) Cor. (C)
I. Solo. ppp
con sord.
dim.
C.à p. (Es)
Tr. (Es)
Tbni.
Tb.
Timp.
due sonatori de' timpani coi bacchetti di spugna. - rullante.
G. C.
arco
Vl. I
Vl. II
Vla.
Vc.
Cb.

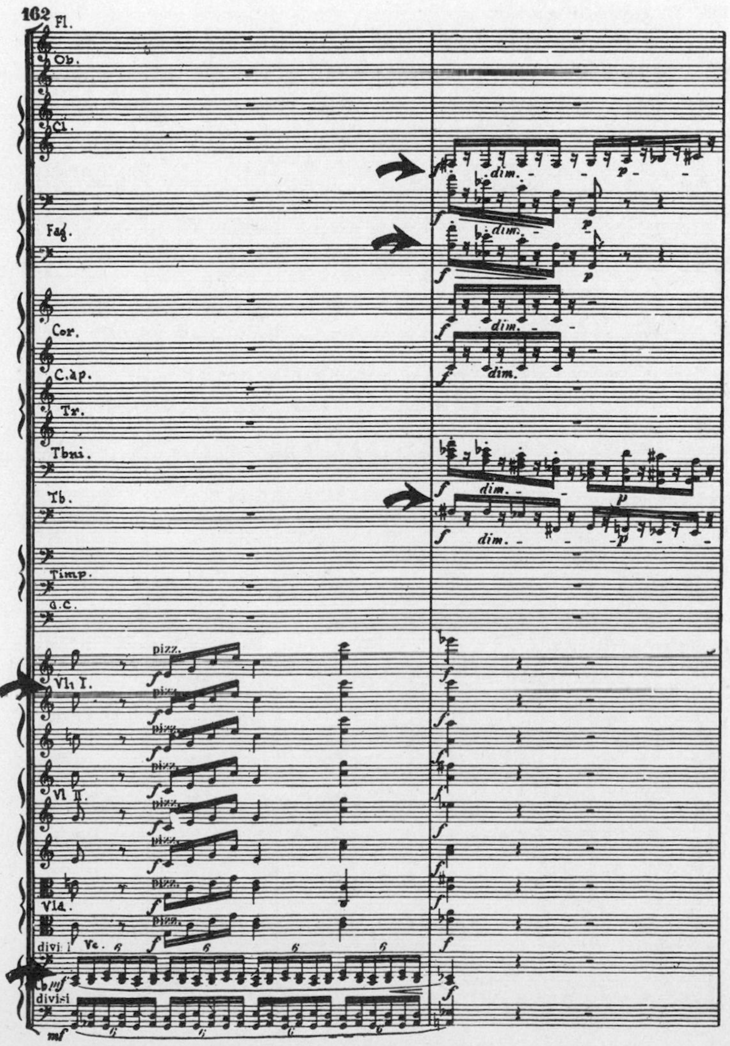
Fl.
Ob.
Cl.
Fag.
dim.
Cor.
C. à p.
Tr.
Tbni.
Tb.
Timp.
G. C.
pizz.
Vl. I.
Vl. II.
Vla.
divisi
Vc.
Cb.

Fl.
Fl. gr.
Fl. Picc.
Fl. picc.
Cl.
Fg.
Cor.
C. à p.
Tr.
Tbni.
Timp.
G. C.
Vl. I.
Vl. II.
Vla.
Vc.
Cb.

165
Fl.
Ob.
poco f>p
(Es)
Cl.
(C)
Fg.
Cor.
C.à p.
Tr.
Tbni.
Tb.
Timp.
G.C.
Vl. I
Vl. II
Vla.
Vc.
Cb.

166
Fl.
a 2.
I. Solo.
Ob.
dim.
Cl.
Fg.
pp
Cor.
Càp.
Tr.
Tbni.
Tb.
Timp.
G.C.
Vl. I.
Vl. II
Vla.
divisi

167
Allegro. M.M. ♩. = 112.
gr. e picc.
Fl.
Ob.
Cl.
(C)
Solo.
ppp
Fg.
I. II.
III. IV.
con sord.
Solo.
dimin.
Cor.
(C)
Tbni.
Tb.
Timp.
G.C.
pp
IDÉE FIXE
Cl.
(C)
cresc.
Timp.
cresc. poco a poco
G.C.
div.
Vl. II
Vla
Vc.
Cb.

168
Allegro assai. M.M. 𝅗𝅥 = 76.
Fl.
a 2.
Cl.
Fg.
Cor.
senza sord.
Càp.
Tr.
Tbni.
a 3.
Tb.
Timp.
G.C.
Vl. I.
Vl. II.
Vla
Vc.
Cb.
BRIDGE PASSAGE

PARAPHRASE IDEE FIXE

INTERMEDIATE THEME

173
Picc.
Fl.
Ob.
(Es) Cl. (C)
Fg.
(Es) Cor. (C)
C.à p. (Es)
Tr. (Es)
Tbni.
Tb.
Timp.
G.C.
Vl.
Vla.
Vc.
Cb.
175
a 2.
174
unis.
176

Lontano.

DIES IRAE.

DIES IRAE—FIRST STATEMENT

sempre senza stringendo

181
Cmp.
Picc.
Fl.
Ob.
(Es)
Cl.
(C)
Fg.
(Es)
Cor.
(C)
C.à p.
(Es)
Tr.
(Es)
Tbni.
(C)
Tb.
(B)
Timp.
G.C.
Vl.
Vla.
Vc.
Cb.
pizz.
pizz.
pizz.

182
Cmp.
Fl.
Ob.
a 2
Clar.
Fag.
Tbni.
arco
Viol.
arco
Vla.
arco
Vc.
arco
Cb.
pizz.
pizz.
Cmp.
Oph.
Vcll.
Cb.

183
Cmp.
Picc.
Fl.
Ob.
(Es)
Cl.
(C)
Fg.
(Es)
Cor.
(C)
C.à p.
(Es)
Tr.
(Es)
Tbni.
(C)
Tb.
(B)
Timp.
G.C.
pizz.
Vl.
pizz.
pizz.
Vla.
Vo.
Cb.

184
Cmp.
Picc.
Fl.
Ob.
Cl.
Fg.
Cor.
C.à p.
Tr.
Tbni.
Tb.
Timp.
G.C.
arco
Vl.
arco
Vla.
arco
Vc.
arco
ten.
Cb.
arco
ten.

185
Cmp.
Fg.
(C)
Tb.
(B)
G.C.
Vc.
Cb.
Cmp.
Fg.
(Es)
Cor.
(C)
Tr.
(Es)
Tbni.
(C)
Tb.
(B)
G.C.
Vc.
Cb.

186
Cmp.
Picc.
Fl.
Ob.
Cl.
Fg.
Tr.
Tbni.
Tb.
Timp.
G.C.
Vl.
Vla.
Vc.
Cb.
pizz.

187
Cmp.
Picc.
Fl.
Ob.
(Es)
Cl.
(C)
Fg.
(Es)
Cor.
(C)
C.à p.
(Es)
Tr.
(Es)
Tbni.
(C)
Tb.
(B)
Timp.
due sonatori de' timpani coi bacchetti di spugna.
rullante.
G.C.
arco
Vl.
Vla.
Vc.
Cb.

188
Cor.
Cornet.
a 2
Tr.
G.C.
Viol.
Vla.
Vell.
Fag.
unis.
cresc.
Cor.
Cornet.
Tr.
Timp.
G.C.
Viol.
Vla.
Vc.
Cb.

189

191

190

Ronde du Sabbat.

un poco rit. M.M. 𝅗𝅥. 104.

192

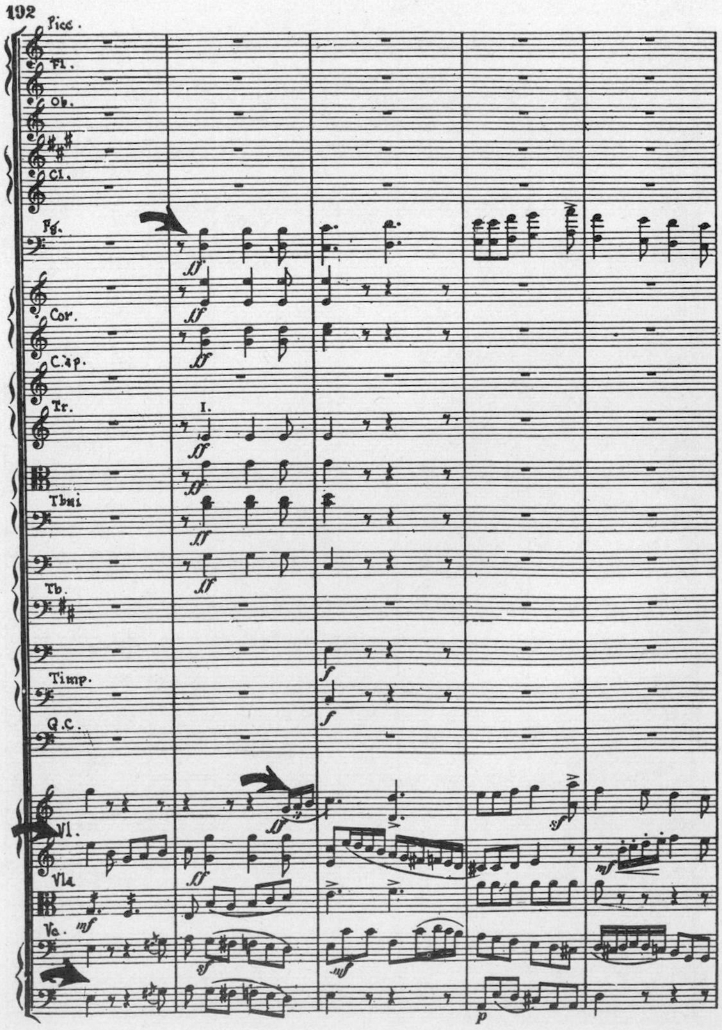

193

194

195

196

197
198
199
200
Picc.
Fl.
Ob.
(Es) Cl. (C)
Fg.
(Es) Cor. (C)
C.à p. (Es)
Tr. (Es)
Tbni.
(C) Tb. (B)
Timp.
G.C.
Vl.
Vla.
Vc.
Cb.
p cresc.
a 2
unis

201

202

203

204

205

206

207

208

209

211

210

212

213

215

214

(Dies irae et Ronde du Sabbat.)

DIES IRAE COMBINED WITH PRINCIPAL THEME

216

217
Picc.
Fl.
Ob.
(Es)
(C)
Fg.
(Es)
Cor.
(C)
C.a.p.
(Es)
Tr.
(Es)
Tbni.
(C)
Tb.
(B)
Timp.
G.C.
Vl.
Vla.
Vc.
Cb.

218
Picc
Fl
Ob.
Cl.
Fg.
Cor.
Tr.
Tbni.
Tb.
Timp
G.C.
Vl.
Vla.
Vc.
Cb.

219
Fl.
Vl.
Vla.
Vc.
Cb.
Picc.
Fl.
Ob.
(Es)
Cl.
(C)
Fg.
Vl.
Vla.
Vc.
Cb.

220
Fl.
Ob.
Cl. in C.
Fag.
col legno
col legno
col legno
Vc.
Cb.
div.
a 2
Fl.
Ob.
Cl.
Fag.
Vl
Vla.
Vcl. div.
pizz.
Cb.
pizz.

221
Fl.
Ob.
Cl.
(C)
Fg.
Vl.
Vla.
Vc.
Cb.
arco

222
Picc.
Fl. Solo
p legg.
a 2
Cl.
Cor.
C.àp.
Tr.
Tbni.
Tb.
Timp.
G.C.
Vl.
Vla.
Vc.
Cb.

223
Picc.
Fl.
Ob.
(Es)
Cl.
(C)
Fg.
Cor.
C.àp.
(Es)
Tr.
Tbni.
Tb.
(B)
Timp.
G.C.
arco
Vl.
Vla.
Vc.
Cb.

224
Picc.
Fl.
Ob.
Cl.
mf
cresc.
Fag.
unis.
Cor.
C.àp.
a 2
Tr.
Tbni.
Tb.
Timp.
G.C.
Vla.
Vc.
Cb.
pp cresc.

animando un poco

229

Picc.
Fl.
Ob.
(Es)
Cl.
(C)
Fg.
(Es)
Cor.
(C)
a2
C.à p.
(Es)
Tr.
(Es)
Tbni.
(C)
Tb.
(B)
Timp.
G.C.
Vl.
Vla.
Vc.
Cb.
div.

231

Picc.
Fl.
Ob.
(Es)
Cl.
(C)
unis.
Fg.
(Es)
Cor.
(C)
C.à p.
(Es)
Tr.
(Es)
Tbni.
a2
(C)
Tb.
(B)
Timp.
G.C.
Vl.
Vla.
Vc.
Cb.
ten.

230

Picc.
Fl.
Ob.
Cl
Fg.
Cor.
C.àp.
Tr.
Tbni.
Tb.
Timp.
G.C.
Vl.
Vla.
Vc.
Cb.

SYMPHONY No. 1, Op. 38 ("Spring") — *ROBERT SCHUMANN*

MOVEMENTS:

I. *Andante-Allegro molto vivace*

II. *Larghetto*

III. *Scherzo-Molto vivace*

IV. *Allegro animato e grazioso*

Symphony No. I is scored for the following instruments:

2 Flauti (Flutes)	*Fl.*	3 Timpani (Tympani)	*Timp.*
2 Oboi (Oboes)	*Ob.*	Triangolo (Triangle)	*Trgl.*
2 Clarinetti (Clarinets)	*Cl.*	1. Violini (1st Violins)	*Vl.*
2 Fagotti (Bassoons)	*Fg.*	2. Violini (2nd Violins)	*Vl.*
4 Corni (Horns)	*Cor.*	Violi (Violas)	*Vla.*
2 Trombe (Trumpets)	*Tr.*	Violoncelli (Violoncellos)	*Vc.*
3 Tromboni (Trombones)	*Tbn.*	Contrabassi (Double Basses)	*Cb.*

Each instrument is listed above under its name as printed on the first page of the score; its English equivalent, and the abbreviation used on succeeding pages.

This symphony, which Schumann himself characterized as a "Spring Symphony", was completed in 1841, and first performed at the Gewandhaus Concerts in Leipzig under Mendelssohn's direction on March 31st of that year.

In a letter to Wilhelm Taubert, who was to conduct the symphony in Berlin, Schumann wrote as follows on January 10, 1843: "Could you imbue your orchestra with something of the springtime mood which I had particularly in mind when I completed the symphony in February 1841? The trumpet call at the entrance I should like to have sound as if it came from on high, like an awakening summons". It is also claimed that the composer had the following subtitles in mind: "Spring's Beginning" for the first movement, "Evening" for the second, "Merry Companions" for the third and "Spring at the Full" for the last movement.

Clara Schumann, the composer's wife, as well as a famous pianist and an able composer, wrote as follows after the first performance: "My husband's symphony achieved a triumph over all cabals and intrigues; I never heard a symphony received with such applause".

The "Spring" Symphony is recorded by the Chicago Symphony Orchestra under the direction of Frederick Stock.

Symphony No 1
("Spring")

I   Robert Schumann, Op. 38

1

INTRODUCTION—SECTION I

3

2

4

un poco ritard.
5
I Solo
Fl.
Ob.
Cl.
Fg.
(F) Cor. (B)
p dolce
dim.
Tr. (B)
Tbn.
Timp.
Trgl.
Vl.
Vla.
Vc.
Cb.
pizz.
arco
INTRODUCTION—SECTION 2

6
20
a tempo
Fl.
Ob.
Cl. (B)
Fag.
(F) Cor. (B)
Vl.
pizz.
arco
Vla.
Vc.
Cb.
Piu vivace e poco a poco accelerando
Fl.
Cl. (B)
Fag.
Cor. (B)
cresc.
dim.
cresc. poco
cresc. poco a poco
INTRODUCTION—SECTION 3

7
30
Fl.
Ob.
Cl.
Fg.
(F) Cor. (B)
Tr. (B)
Tbn.
Timp.
Trgl.
Vl.
mf cresc. sino al
a poco
Vla.
Vc.
Cb.
cresc.

8
Fl.
Ob.
Cl.
Fg.
(F) Cor. (B)
Tr. (B)
Tbn.
Timp.
Trgl.
Vl.
Vla.
Vc.
Cb.
cresc.

Allegro molto vivace (♩= 120)
EXPOSITION
9
40
Fl.
Ob.
Cl.
Fg.
(F) Cor. (B)
Tr. (B)
Tbn.
Timp.
Trgl.
Vl.
Vla.
Vc.
Cb.
PRINCIPAL THEME—PART I, 1st PERIOD
11
60
a 2
cresc.
PRINCIPAL THEME—PART II
10
50
PRINCIPAL THEME—PART I, 2nd PERIOD
12
cresc.

13
14
15
16
70
80
90
100
110
Fl.
Ob.
Cl.
Fg.
Cor.
Tr.
Tbn.
Timp.
Trgl.
Vl.
Vla.
Vc.
Cb.
dim.
p dolce
p sempre
pizz.
arco
cresc.
SUBORDINATE THEME—PART I
SUBORDINATE
THEME—PART II

17

18

CODETTA

19

20

DEVELOPMENT

DEVELOPMENT—SECTION I

21
Fl.
Ob.
Cl. (B)
Fag.
Cor. (F)
Vl.
Vla.
Vc. e Cb.
140
150
I. II. a 2
pizz.
arco
dolce
stacc.
DEVELOPMENT—SECTION 2

22
Ob.
Cl. (B)
Fag.
Cor. (B)
Vl.
Vla.
Vc. e Cb.
160
170
III. IV.
arco
stacc.
cresc.
Fl.
(F) Cor. (B)
a 2

23
Fl.
Ob.
Cl.
Fg.
(F) Cor. (B)
Tr. (B)
Tbn.
Timp.
Trgl.
Vl.
Vla.
Vc.
Cb.
a 2
cresc.
DEVELOPMENT—SECTION 3

24
Fl.
Ob.
Cl.
Fg.
(F) Cor. (B)
Tr. (B)
Tbn.
Timp.
Trgl.
Vl.
Vla.
Vc.
Cb.
180
I. Solo
leggiero
pizz.

25
190
Fl.
Ob.
Cl.
Fg.
(F) Cor. (B)
Tr. (B)
Tbn.
Timp.
Trgl.
Vl.
Vla.
Vc.
Cb.
I. Solo
leggiero
arco
pizz.
26
a2
27
a 2
200
Solo
DEVELOPMENT—SECTION 4
28
210
I.

29

220
Fl.
Ob.
Cl.
Fg.
(F) Cor. (B)
Vl.
Vla.
Vc.
Cb.
pizz.
arco
stacc.
a 2
cresc.
DEVELOPMENT—SECTION 5

30

230
240
Fl.
Ob.
Cl.
Fg.
(F) Cor. (B)
Vl.
Vla.
Vc.
Cb.
poco a poco
cresc.
stacc.
III. IV.

31

Fl.
Ob.
Cl.
Fg.
(F) Cor. (B)
Tr. (B)
Tbn.
Timp.
Trgl.
Vl.
Vla.
Vc.
Cb.
cresc.
DEVELOPMENT—SECTION 6

32

250
Fl.
Ob.
Cl.
Fg.
(F) Cor. (B)
Tr. (B)
Tbn.
Timp.
Trgl.
Vl.
Vla.
Vc.
Cb.
cresc.
p cresc.

Fl.
Ob.
Cl.
Fg.
(F) Cor. (B)
Tr. (B)
Tbn.
Timp.
Trgl.
Vl.
Vla.
Vc.
Cb.
1.
cresc.
dim.
pizz.

260
Fl.
Ob.
Cl.
Fg.
(F) Cor. (B)
Tr. (B)
Tbn.
Timp.
Trgl.
Vl.
Vla.
Vc.
Cb.
a 2
cresc.
p poco a poco cresc.
arco

270
Fl.
Ob.
Cl.
Fg.
(F) Cor. (B)
Tr. (B)
Tbn.
Timp.
Trgl.
Vl.
Vla.
Vc.
Cb.
cresc.
a 2

280
Fl.
Ob.
Cl.
Fg.
(F) Cor. (B)
Tr. (B)
Tbn.
Timp.
Trgl.
Vl.
Vla.
Vc.
Cb.
cresc.

THEME—PART I, 1st PERIOD

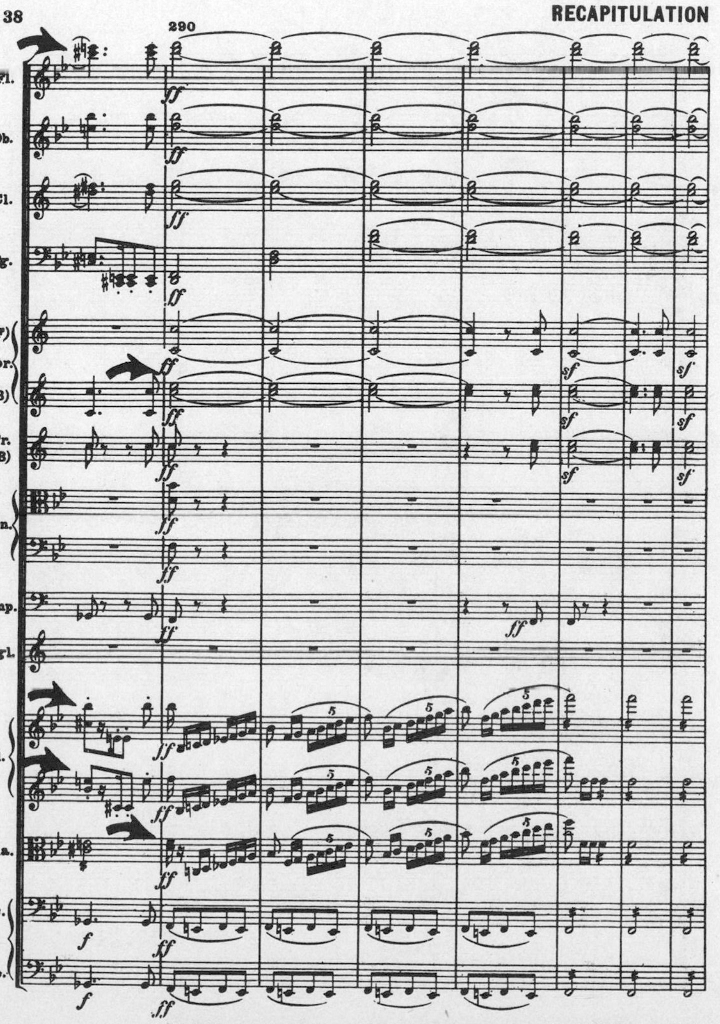

RETURNING PASSAGE (RETRANSITION) ~~~~ RETURN PRINCIPAL

41

RETURN PRINCIPAL THEME—PART II

42

43

44

RETURN SUBORDINATE THEME—PART I

Animato **CODA**

Poco a poco stringendo

390
Fl.
Ob.
Cl.
Fg.
(F)
Cor.
(B)
Tr.
(B)
Tbn.
Timp.
Trgl.
Vl.
Vla.
Vc.
Cb.
cresc.

400
Fl.
Ob.
Cl.
Fg.
(F)
Cor.
(B)
Tr.
(B)
Tbn.
Timp.
Trgl.
Vl.
Vla.
Vc.
Cb.
f

410
Fl.
Ob.
Cl.
Fg.
(F)
Cor.
(B)
Tr.
(B)
Tbn.
Timp.
Trgl.
Vl.
Vla.
Vc.
Cb.
f
p
fp
cresc.

420
Fl.
Ob.
Cl.
Fg.
(F)
Cor.
(B)
Tr.
(B)
Tbn.
Timp.
Trgl.
Vl.
Vla.
Vc.
Cb.
cresc.

53

Fl.
Ob.
Cl.
Fg.
(F) Cor. (B)
Tr. (B)
Tbn.
Timp.
Trgl.
Vl.
Vla.
Vc.
Cb.

54

430
Fl.
Ob.
Cl.
Fg.
(F) Cor. (B)
Tr. (B)
Tbn.
Timp.
Trgl.
Vl.
Vla.
Vc.
Cb.
dim.
diminuendo
sempre

55

440
Fl.
Ob.
Cl.
Fg.
(F) Cor. (B)
Tr. (B)
Tbn.
Timp.
Trgl.
Vl.
Vla.
Vc.
Cb.
pizz.
arco
fp dolce
cresc.
CODA—SECTION 2

56

450
Fl.
Ob.
Cl.
Fg.
(F) Cor. (B)
Tr. (B)
Tbn.
Timp.
Trgl.
Vl.
Vla.
Vc.
Cb.
cresc.
a 2
div.

57
460
58
470
CODA—SECTION 3
I. Solo
480
p dolce
CODA—SECTION 4
59
490
marc.
cresc.
60
500
sempre
f sempre
Fl.
Ob.
Cl.
Fg.
Cor.
Tr.
Tbn.
Timp.
Trgl.
Vl.
Vla.
Vc.
Cb.
Fag.
dim.
pizz.
arco

61
Fl.
Ob.
Cl.
Fg.
(F)
Cor.
(B)
Tr.
(B)
Tbn.
Timp.
Trgl.
Vl.
Vla.
Vc.
Cb.

62
510
Fl.
Ob.
Cl.
Fg.
(F)
Cor.
(B)
Tr.
(B)
Tbn.
Timp.
Trgl.
Vl.
Vla.
Vc.
Cb.

Larghetto (♪=66)
II
63
2 Flauti
2 Oboi
2 Clarinetti in B
2 Fagotti
2 Corni in Es
3 Tromboni
Alto
Tenore
Basso
I
Violino
II
Viola
Violoncello e Contrabasso
PRINCIPAL THEME—PART I
10
Fl.
Ob.
Cl. (B)
Fag.
Cor. (Es)
Vl.
Vla.
Vc. e Cb.
cresc.
PRINCIPAL THEME—PART II

64
Fl.
Ob.
Cl. (B)
Fag.
Cor. (Es)
Vl.
Vla.
Vc. e Cb.
cresc.
20

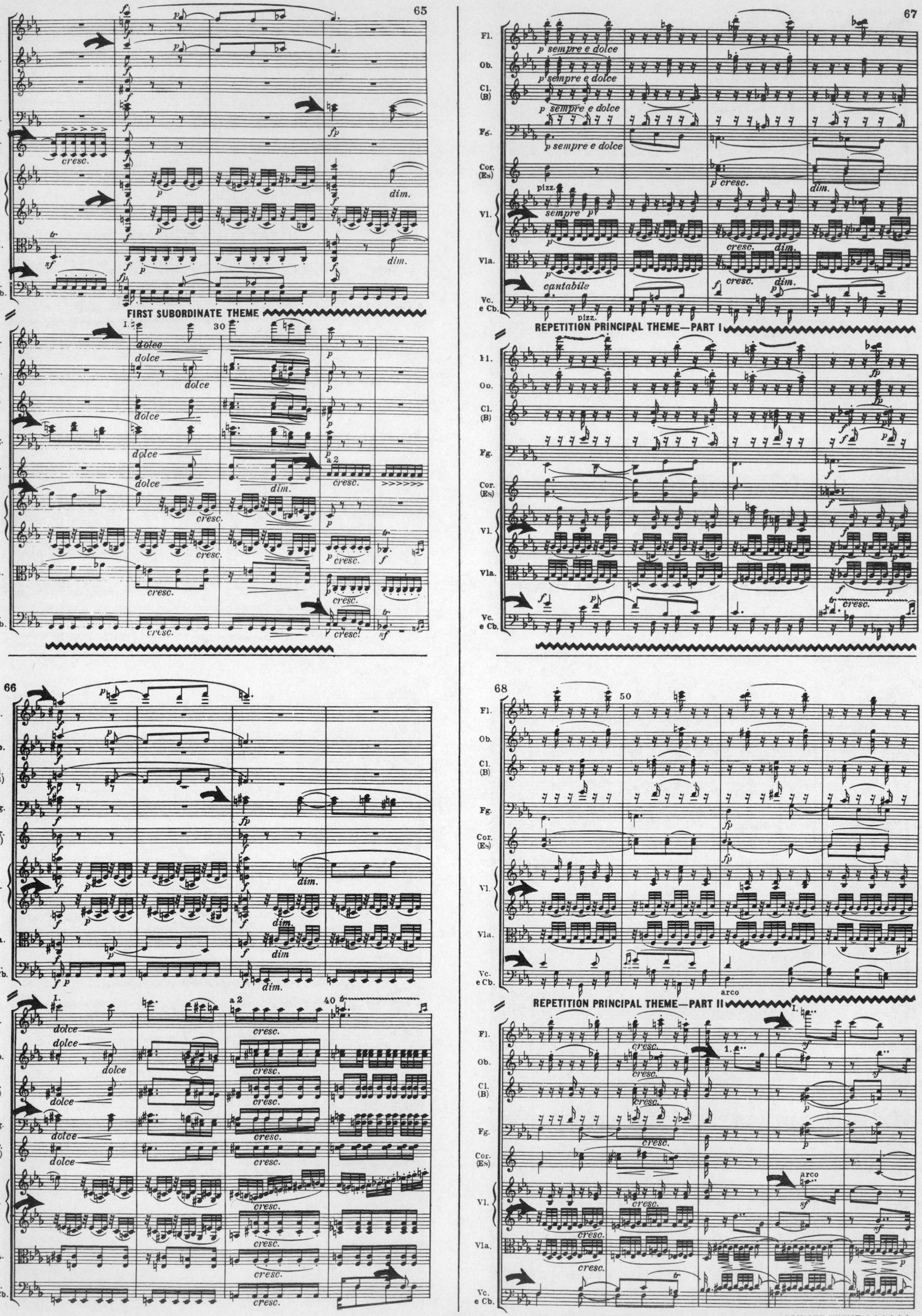
65
66
67
68
FIRST SUBORDINATE THEME
REPETITION PRINCIPAL THEME—PART I
REPETITION PRINCIPAL THEME—PART II
SECOND SUBORDINATE THEME
Fl.
Ob.
Cl. (B)
Fag.
Cor. (Es)
Vl.
Vla.
Vc. e Cb.
p sempre e dolce
cantabile
pizz.
arco
dolce
cresc.
dim.

RETURNING PASSAGE (RETRANSITION)

RETURN PRINCIPAL THEME—PART II

90
Ob.
Cl. (B)
Fg.
Cor. (Es)
Vl.
Vla.
Vc. e Cb.
Fl.
sf
dim.
f

CODA
Fl.
Ob.
Cl.
Fg.
Cor. (Es)
Tbn.
Vl.
Vla.
Vc.
Cb.
sf
fp
f
p
CODA—SECTION 1

Fl.
Ob.
Cl. (B)
Fg.
Cor. (Es)
Vl.
Vla.
Vc. e Cb.
dolce
100
sf
dim.
cresc.
pp
pizz.

110
Fl.
Ob.
Cl.
Fag.
Cor. (Es)
Tbn.
Vl.
Vla.
Vc.
Cb.
p dolce
pp dolce
dim.
pp
f
p
pizz.
CODA—SECTION 2
CODA—SECTION 3

III. Scherzo

Molto vivace (♩. = 88) **PRINCIPAL SECTION**

PRINCIPAL THEME—PART I, 1st PERIOD PRIN-

CIPAL THEME—PART I, 2nd PERIOD

PRINCIPAL THEME—PART II

PRIN—

CIPAL THEME—PART III, 1st PERIOD PRIN—

CIPAL THEME—PART III, 2nd PERIOD

FIRST SUBORDINATE THEME—PART I, 1st PERIOD FIRST SUBORDINATE THEME—

85

PART I, 2nd PERIOD

87

PERIOD

FIRST SUBORDI-

86

FIRST SUBORDINATE THEME—PART II, 1st

88

NATE THEME—PART II, 2nd PERIOD

FIRST SUBORDINATE THEME—PART III, 1st PERIOD

FIRST SUBORDINATE THEME—PART III, 2nd PERIOD

REPETITION FIRST SUBORDINATE THEME—PART II

REPETITION FIRST SUBORDINATE THEME—PART III

97
200
Fl.
Ob.
Cl.
Fg.
(D) Cor. (B)
Tr. (D)
Tbn.
Timp.
Vl.
Vla.
Vc.
Cb.
cresc.

98
210
220
Fl.
Ob.
Cl.
Fg.
(D) Cor. (B)
Tr. (D)
Tbn.
Timp.
Vl.
Vla.
Vc.
Cb.
cresc.

99
230
a 2
Fl.
Ob.
Cl.
Fg.
(D) Cor. (B)
Tr. (D)
Tbn.
Timp.
Vl.
Vla.
Vc.
Cb.
cresc.
Da capo il Scherzo (P. 78)
e poi il Trio II (P. 100)

100
TRIO II
240
Fl.
Ob.
Cl.
Fg.
(D) Cor. (B)
Tr. (D)
Tbn.
Timp.
Vl.
Vla.
Vc.
Cb.
cresc.
SECOND SUBORDINATE THEME—PART I
SECOND SUBORDI+

NATE THEME—PART II

SECOND SUBOR—

DINATE THEME—PART III

CODETTA—1st PERIOD

105

CODETTA—2nd PERIOD

106

RETURN PRINCIPAL THEME—PART I

107

108

CODA

CODA—SECTION I

CODA—SECTION 2

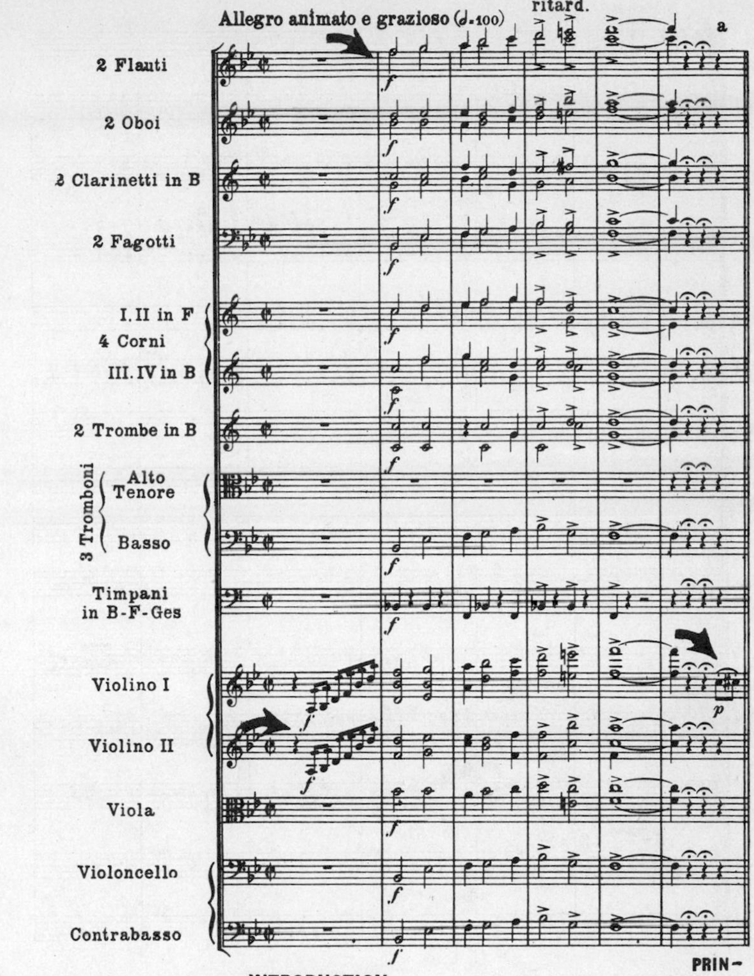

PRIN-

INTRODUCTION

EXPOSITION

CIPAL THEME—PART I, 1st PERIOD

113

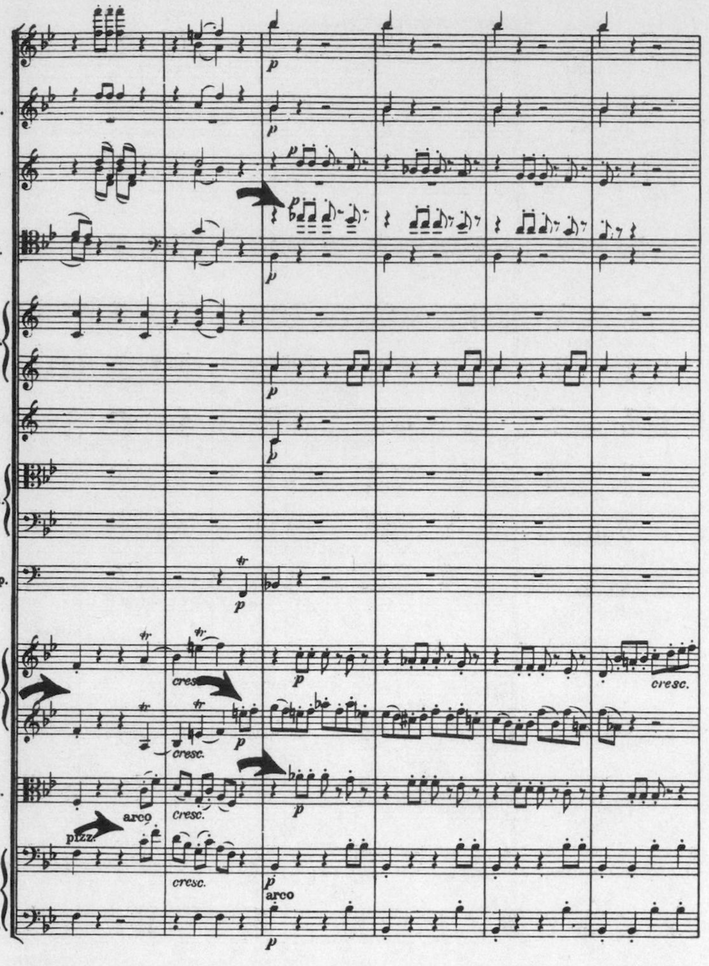

PRINCIPAL THEME—PART I, 2nd PERIOD

114

115

116

PRINCIPAL THEME—PART II

117

118

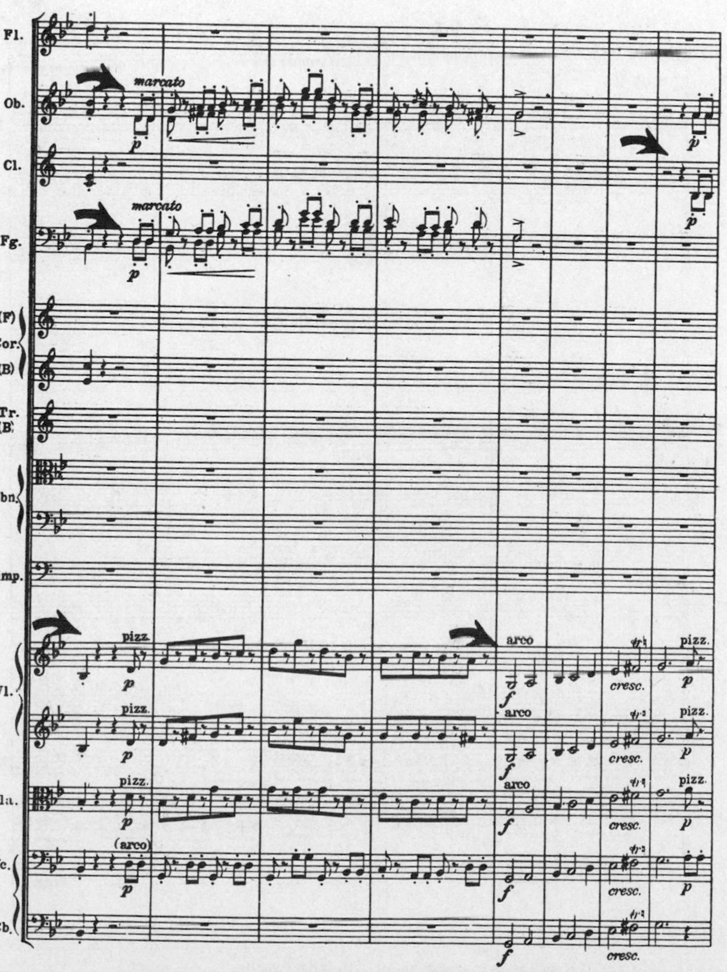

SUBORDINATE THEME—PART I, 1st PERIOD SUB

119

ORDINATE THEME—PART I, 2nd PERIOD SUB—

ORDINATE THEME—PART II

120

CODETTA—PART I

121

123

CODETTA

122

124

PART II

125

126 DEVELOPMENT

DEVELOPMENT—SECTION 1

DEVELOPMENT—SECTION 2

127

DEVELOPMENT—SECTION 3

128

DEVELOPMENT—SECTION 4

RETURNING PASSAGE (RETRANSITION)

RETURN PRINCIPAL THEME—PART I, 1st PERIOD

RE—

TURN PRINCIPAL THEME—PART I, 2nd PERIOD

RETURN PRINCIPAL THEME—

PART II

RETURN SUBORDINATE

THEME—PART I, 1st PERIOD RETURN SUBORDINATE

THEME—PART I, 2nd PERIOD RETURN SUBORDI

141

NATE THEME—PART II

143

142

RETURN CODETTA—PART I

144

145

RETURN CODETTA—PART II

Poco a poco accelerando

147

CODA—SECTION I

146

148

149

151

150

152

153

155

CODA—SECTION 2

154

156

157
330
Fl.
Ob.
Cl.
Fg.
(F)
Cor.
(B)
Tr.
(B)
Tbn.
Timp.
Vl.
Vla.
Vc.
Cb.
CODA—SECTION 3

158
340
a 2
G.P.
Fl.
Ob.
Cl.
Fg.
(F)
Cor.
(B)
Tr.
(B)
Tbn.
Timp.
Vl.
Vla.
Vc.
Cb.

SYMPHONY IN D MINOR

CÉSAR FRANCK

MOVEMENTS:

I. *Lento-Allegro non troppo*

II. *Allegretto*

III. *Allegro non troppo*

This symphony is scored for the following instruments:

2 Flauti (Flutes)	*Fl.*
2 Oboi (Oboes)	*Ob.*
1 Corno inglese (English Horn)	*Cor. igl.*
2 Clarinetti (Clarinets)	*Cl.*
1 Clarinetto basso (Bass Clarinet)	*Cl. b.*
2 Fagotti (Bassoons)	*Fg.*
4 Corni (Horns)	*Cor.*
2 Trombe (Trumpets)	*Tr.*
2 Cornetti à pistons (Cornets)	*C. à p.*
3 Tromboni (Trombones)	*Trb.*
1 Tuba (Tuba)	*Tb.*
3 Timpani (Tympani)	*Tp.*
1 Arpa (Harp)	*Arp.*
1. Violini (1st Violins)	*Viol.*
2. Violini (2nd Violins)	*Viol.*
Violi (Violas)	*Vla.*
Violoncelli (Violoncellos)	*Vcl.*
Contrabassi (Double Basses)	*Ctb.*

Each instrument is listed above under its name as printed on the first page of the score; its English equivalent, and the abbreviation used on succeeding pages.

This symphony was composed in 1888; it was completed on August 22nd of that year, and first performed at the Paris Conservatory on February 17, 1889.

In his biography of César Franck, Vincent d'Indy writes as follows of its reception at the first performance: "The performance was quite against the wish of most members of the famous orchestra, and was only pushed through thanks to the benevolent obstinacy of the conductor, Jules Garcin. The subscribers could make neither head nor tail of it, and the music critics were much in the same position. I inquired of one of them—a professor at the Conservatory, and a kind of factotum on the committee—what he thought of the work. 'That a symphony?' he replied in contemptuous tones, 'Who ever heard of writing for the English horn in a symphony? Just mention a single symphony by Haydn or Beethoven introducing the English horn. There, well, you see—your Franck's music may be whatever you please, but it will certainly never be a symphony!' ". Charles Gounod is said to have remarked that the symphony was the affirmation of impotence pushed to dogma.

There are two excellent recordings of this symphony: one by the Lamoureux Orchestra under the direction of Albert Wolff, and another by the Philadelphia Orchestra under the baton of Leopold Stokowski.

1

Symphony in D Minor

I

EXPOSITION

César Franck

2

3

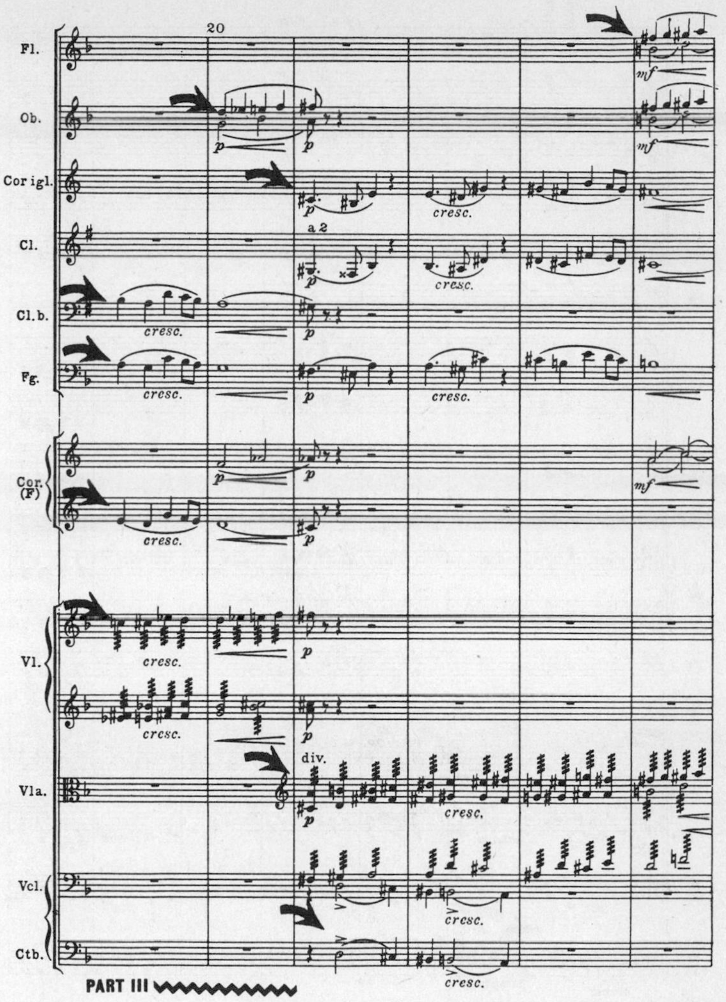

4

5

7

REPETITION PRINCIPAL THEME—PART I

6

8

REPETITION PRINCIPAL THEME—PART II

9

REPETITION PRINCIPAL THEME—PART III

10

11

REPETITION PRINCIPAL THEME—

12

PART IV

13
poco rall.
molto cresc.
dim. pp
BRIDGE PASSAGE
a tempo
100
1. espress.
molto cantabile
dolce
sostenuto
cantabile
SUBORDINATE THEME—PART I
14
110
15
120
marcato
molto sosten.
16
130
f molto cresc.
ff sosten.
SUBORDINATE THEME—

17

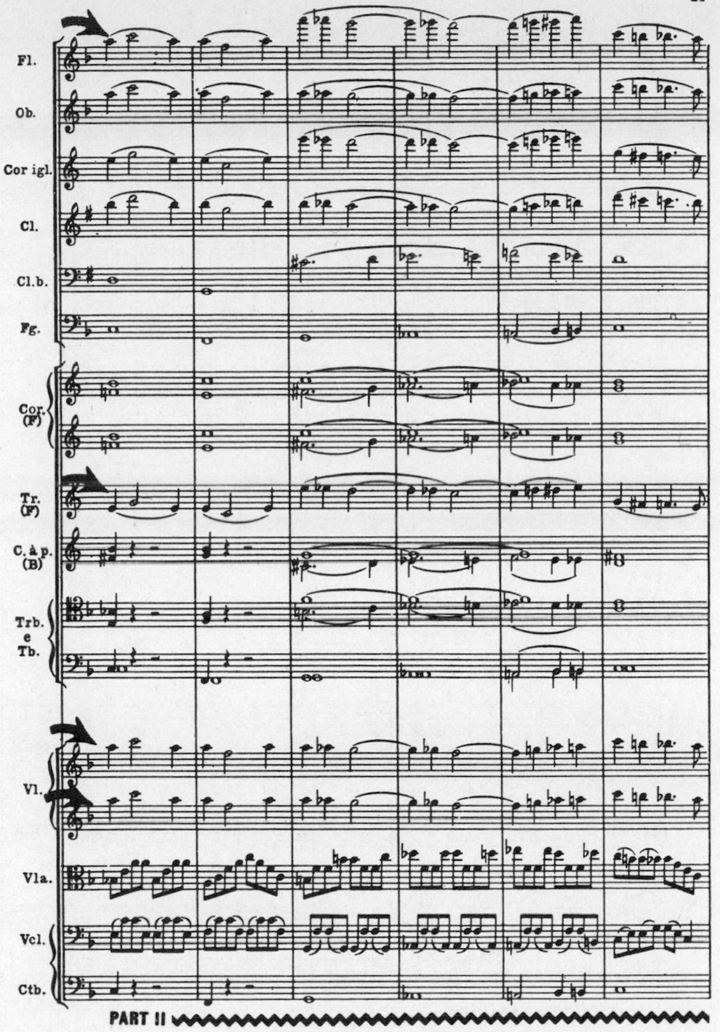
Fl.
Ob.
Cor igl.
Cl.
Cl. b.
Fg.
Cor. (F)
Tr. (F)
C. à p. (B)
Trb. e Tb.
Vl.
Vla.
Vcl.
Ctb.
PART II

18

140
Fl.
Ob.
Cor igl.
Cl.
Cl. b.
Fg.
Cor. (F)
Tr. (F)
C. à p. (B)
Trb. e Tb.
a 2
Vl.
Vla.
Vcl.
Ctb.

19

Fl.
Ob.
Cor igl.
Cl.
Cl. b.
Fg.
Cor. (F)
Tr. (F)
C. à p. (B)
Trb. e Tb.
mf
Vl.
Vla.
Vcl.
Ctb.
CODETTA—PART I

20

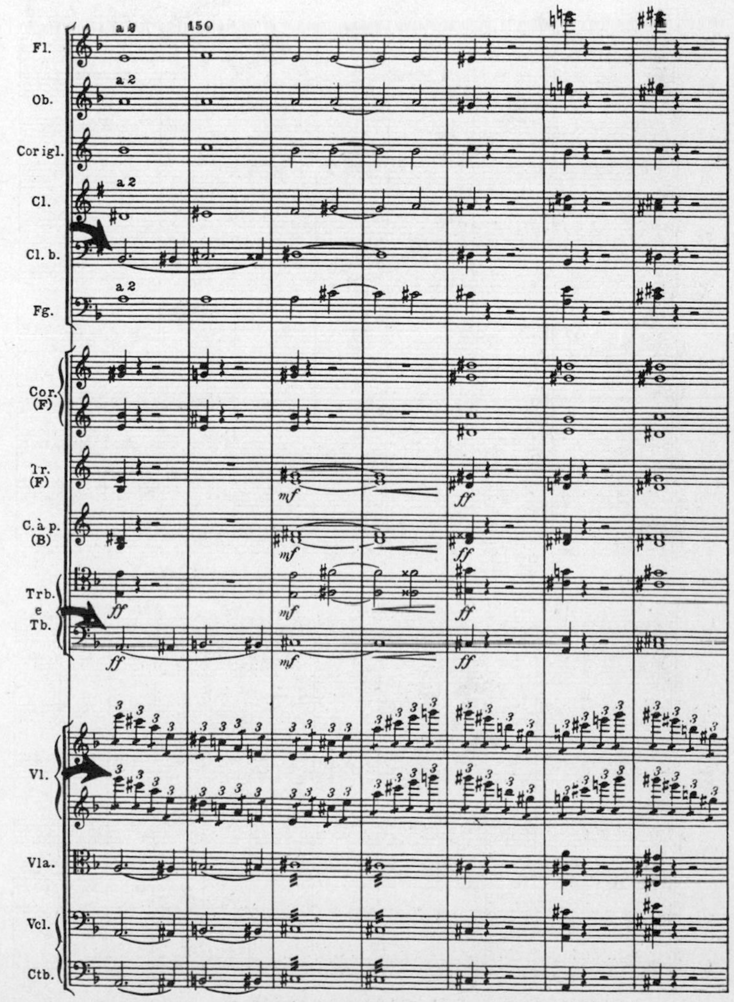
a 2
150
Fl.
Ob.
Cor igl.
Cl.
Cl. b.
Fg.
Cor. (F)
Tr. (F)
C. à p. (B)
Trb. e Tb.
ff
mf
Vl.
Vla.
Vcl.
Ctb.

21
160
Fl.
Ob.
Cor igl.
Cl.
Cl.b.
Fg.
Cor. (F)
Tr. (F)
C. à p. (B)
Trb. e Tb.
Vl.
Vla.
Vcl.
Ctb.
a 2
dim.
molto dim.
espress.
molto dolce

23
190
Fl.
Ob.
Cor igl.
Cl.
Fg.
Cor. (F)
Vl.
Vla.
Vcl.
Cl.b.
dolciss.
pp
p
sf cresc.
mf cresc.
p cresc.
TION I
DEVELOPMENT—
SECTION 2
DEVELOPMENT—

22
170
180
Fl.
Ob.
Cor igl.
Cl.
Fg.
Cor. (F)
Vl.
Vla.
Vcl.
Ctb.
Cl.b.
p espress.
pp
div.
pizz.
dolce
DEVELOPMENT
CODETTA—PART II
DEVELOPMENT—SEC

24
200
Fl.
Ob.
Cor igl.
Cl.
Cl. b.
Fg.
Cor. (F)
Vl.
Vla.
Vcl.
Ctb.
a 2
f marc.
f
SECTION 3

25
Fl.
Ob.
Cor igl.
Cl.
a 2
Cl. b.
Fg.
a 2
Cor. (F)
Vl.
Vla.
Vcl.
f
Ctb.

26
210
a 2
Fl.
f marc.
a 2
Ob.
f marc.
Cor igl.
f
Cl. b.
f
Fg.
mf
Cor. (F)
mf
Tr. (F)
mf
C. à p. (B)
mf
Vl.
f ma cantando
marc.
f ma cantando
Vla.
Vcl.
f
Ctb.
f
DEVELOPMENT—SECTION 4

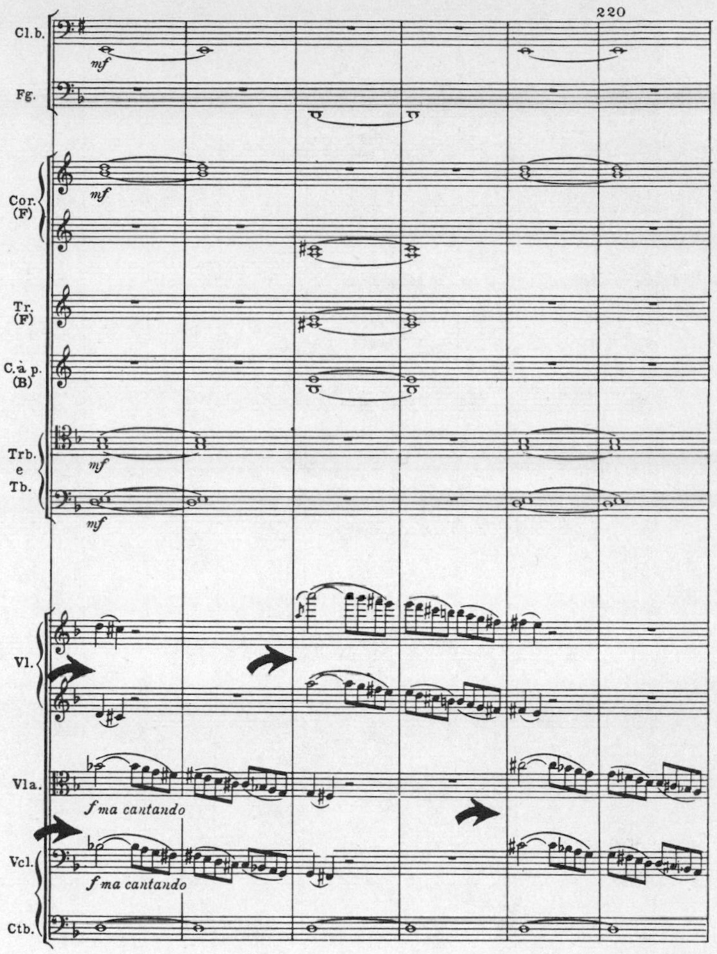
27
220
Cl. b.
mf
Fg.
Cor. (F)
mf
Tr. (F)
C. à p. (B)
Trb. e Tb.
mf
mf
Vl.
Vla.
f ma cantando
Vcl.
f ma cantando
Ctb.

28
a 2
Fl.
f
cresc.
ff
a 2
Ob.
f
cresc.
ff
Cor igl.
f
cresc.
ff
a 2
Cl.
f
cresc.
ff
Cl. b.
f
cresc.
ff
a 2
Fg.
f
cresc.
ff
Cor. (F)
f
cresc.
ff
Tr. (F)
f
cresc.
ff
C. à p. (B)
f
cresc.
ff
Trb. e Tb.
f
cresc.
cresc.
ff
Vl.
sempre f
cresc.
ff
sempre f
cresc.
ff
Vla.
sempre f
cresc.
ff
Vcl.
sempre f
cresc.
ff
Ctb.
sf sempre f
sf
cresc.
sf
ff

29
230
Fl. Ob. Cor igl. Cl. Cl. b. Fg. Cor. (F) Tb. Vl. Vla. Vcl. Ctb.
molto dim.
div.
pizz.
DEVELOPMENT—SECTION 5
30
240
Fl. Ob. Cor igl. Cl. Cl. b. Fg. Cor. (F) Tr. (F) C. à p. (B) Trb. e Tb. Vl. Vla. Vcl. Ctb.
cresc.
unis.
31
Vl. Vla. Vcl.
espress.
molto dim.
arco
DEVELOPMENT—
250
Fl. Ob. Cor igl. Cl. Cl. b. Fg. Cor. (F) Tr. (F) C. à p. (B) Trb. Vl. Vla. Vcl.
Bassi
SECTION 6
32
Fl. Ob. Cor igl. Cl. Cl. b. Fg. Cor. (F) Tr. (F) C. à p. (B) Trb. e Tb. Vl. Vla. Vcl. e Ctb.
espress.

33

espress.
a 2
260
Fl.
Ob.
Cor.igl.
Cl
Cl.b.
Fg.
Cor. (F)
1, 2.
Tr. (F)
C.à p. (B)
Trb. e Tb.
Vl.
Vla.
Vcl.
Ctb.
f
ff

34

Fl.
Ob.
Cor.igl.
Cl.
Cl.b.
Fg.
Cor. (F)
a 2
Tr. (F)
C.à p. (B)
Trb. e Tb.
Vl.
Vla.
Vcl.
Ctb.
DEVELOPMENT—

35

a 2
270
Fl.
Ob.
Cor.igl.
Cl.
Cl.b.
Fg.
Cor. (F)
Tr. (F)
C.à p. (B)
Trb. e Tb.
Vl.
Vla.
Vcl.
Ctb.
sempre ff
SECTION 7

36

Fl.
Ob.
Cor.igl.
Cl.
Cl.b.
Fg.
Cor. (F)
Tr. (F)
C.à p. (B)
a 2
Trb. e Tb.
Vl.
Vla.
Vcl.
Ctb.

280
Fl.
Ob.
Cor.igl.
Cl.
Cl.b.
Fg.
Cor. (F)
Tr. (F)
C.à p. (B)
Trb. e Tb.
Vl.
Vla.
Vcl.
Ctb.
molto dim.
espress.
ten.
pp
div.
sempre pp

290
Fl.
Ob.
Cor.igl.
Cl.
Cl.b.
Fg.
Cor. (F)
Vl.
Vla.
Vcl.
Ctb.
ten.
pp
1.
pp espress.
ppp
1.2.
div
ppp espress.
RETURNING PASSAGE
300
poco cresc.
(RETRANSITION)

a 2
310
Fl.
Ob.
Cor.igl.
Cl.
Cl.b.
Fg.
Cor. (F)
Tr. (F)
C.à p. (B)
Tb.
Tp.
Vl.
Vcl.
mf
1.2. a 2
pp
1.
(G.B)
p espress.
p

Fl.
Ob.
Cor.igl.
Cl.
Cl.b.
Fg.
Cor (F)
Tr. (F)
C.à p. (B)
Trb. e Tb.
(Tb.)
Tp.
Vl.
Vla.
Vcl.
Ctb.
sempre cresc.
a 2
cresc.
p molto sostenuto cresc.
mf cresc.

RECAPITULATION

Lento.

RETURN PRINCIPAL THEME—PART I

RETURN PRINCIPAL THEME—PART II

RETURN PRINCIPAL THEME—PART IV

RETURN SUBORDINATE THEME—PART I

53
400
Fl.
Ob.
Cor. igl.
Cl.
Fg.
Cor. (F)
Vl.
Vla.
Vcl.
Ctb.
Cl. b.
Vcl. e Ctb.
Bassi
cresc.
a 2
1.2.
sempre a 2
div.
molto sosten.

54
410
Fl.
Ob.
Cor. igl.
Cl.
Cl. b
Fg.
Cor. (F)
Vl.
Vla.
Vcl. e Ctb.
a 2
cresc.
marcato
cresc. molto sosten.

55
Fl.
Ob.
Cor. igl.
Cl.
Cl. b.
Fg.
Cor. (F)
Tr. (F)
C. à p. (B)
Trb. e Tb.
Tp.
Vl.
Vla.
Vcl.
Ctb.
a 2
f molto cresc.
ff
ff sostenuto
marcato
RETURN SUBOR–

56
420
Fl.
Ob.
Cor. igl.
Cl.
Cl. b.
Fg.
Cor. (F)
Tr. (F)
C. a p. (B)
Trb. e Tb.
Vl.
Vla
Vcl.
Ctb.
a 2
DINATE THEME—PART II

430
Fl.
Ob.
Cor. igl.
Cl.
Cl. b.
Fg.
Cor. (F)
Tr. (F)
a 2
C. à p. (B)
Trb.
e
Tb.
a 2
Vl.
Vla.
Vcl.
Ctb.

a 2
440
Fl.
Ob.
a 2
Cor. igl.
Cl.
a 2
Cl. b.
Fg.
Cor. (F)
Tr. (F)
mf
ff
C. à p. (B)
Trb.
e
Tb.
a 2
Vl.
Vla.
Vcl.
Ctb.

Fl.
Ob
Cor. igl.
Cl.
Cl. b.
Fg.
Cor. (F)
Tr. (F)
C. à p. (B)
Trb.
e
Tb.
2.
Vl.
Vla.
Vcl.
Ctb.
RETURN CODETTA—PART I

a 2
450
Fl.
dim.
Ob.
a 2
dim.
Cor. igl.
Cl.
a 2
dim.
Cl. b.
Fg.
a 2
Cor. (F)
dim.
Tr. (F)
C. à p. (B)
Trb.
c
Tb.
molto dim.
Vl.
Vla.
Vcl.
Ctb.

61

Fl.
Ob.
Cor. igl.
Cl.
Fg.
Cor. (F)
Vl.
Vla.
Vcl.
Ctb.
espress.
molto dolce
div.
p espress.
pp
460
Poco più lento
dolces.
Vcl
RETURN CODETTA—PART II

63

a 2
490
Fl.
Ob.
Cor. igl.
Cl.
Cl. b.
Fg.
Cor. (F)
Tr. (F)
Tb.
Vl.
Vla.
Vcl. e Ctb.
mf
sempre cresc.

62

piu rall
470
CODA
a tempo
Fl.
Ob.
Cl.
Cl. b.
Fg.
Cor. (F)
Vl.
Vla
Vcl. e Ctb.
dolciss.
1.2.
ppp
CODA—SECTION I
480
Cor. igl.
a 2
cresc.

64

Fl.
Ob.
Cor. igl.
Cl.
Cl. b.
Fg.
Cor. (F)
Tr. (F)
C. à p. (B)
Tb.
Vl.
Vla.
Vcl. e Ctb.
a 2
CODA—SECTION 2

65

67

CODA—SECTION 3

66

68

II

PRINCIPAL THEME—PART I

69

Cor.igl.
Arp.
Vl.
Vla.
Vcl.
Ctb.
mf
p
f
dim.
PRINCIPAL THEME—PART II
FIRST
cantabile
arco
molto cantabile
div.
REPETITION PRINCIPAL THEME—PART I WITH MELODY
SECOND REPETI-

70

Cor.igl.
Cl.
Cor. (F)
Arp.
Vl
Vla.
Vcl.
Ctb.
mf cantabile
div.
pizz.
TION PRINCIPAL THEME—PART I WITH MELODY
FIRST REPE-
Fl.
fespr
dim.
arco
TITION PRINCIPAL THEME—PART II WITH MELODY
SECOND

71

Fl.
Cl.
Cor. (F)
Arp.
Vl.
Vla.
Vcl
Ctb.
pp
REPETITION PRINCIPAL THEME—PART II WITH MELODY
arco
dolce cantabile
pp sosten.
pp sostenuto
FIRST SUBORDINATE THEME—PART I

72

Vl.
Vla.
Vcl.
Ctb.
cresc.
molto dim.
Ob.
Cor.igl.
Cl.
Cl.b.
Fg.
Cor. (F)
Tp.
p espress.
pp
FIRST SUBORDINATE THEME—PART II

FIRST SUBORDINATE THEME—PART III

FIRST SUBORDINATE THEME—PART IV

FIRST SUBORDINATE THEME—PART V

RETURN PRINCIPAL THEME—

RETURN PRINCIPAL THEME—

81
poco rall.
a tempo
rall.
Fl.
Cl.
Cor. (F)
Vl.
Vla.
Vcl.
arco
div.
PART II
110
Fg.
sempre pp
82
Cl.b.
Ctb.
pizz.
a 2
VARIATION PRINCIPAL THEME—PART I
83
120
Ob.
VARIATION PRINCIPAL THEME—PART II
84
130
Cor.igl.
dim.
senza sord.

85
Cl.
a 2
espress. dolce
Cor. (F)
Vl.
arco
Vcl.
SECOND SUBORDINATE THEME—PART I
Fg.
140
senza sord.
Vla.
Vcl. e Ctb.

87
Fl.
Ob.
Cor.igl.
Cl.
Cl.b.
Fg.
Cor. (F)
Vl.
Vla.
Vcl.
Ctb.
dim.
cresc.
p espr
dim. espress.
SUBORDINATE THEME—PART II

86
Fl.
Ob.
Cl.
Fg.
Tr. (F)
Vl.
Vla.
Vcl.
Ctb.
a 2
espress.
Cl.b.
150
cresc.
SECOND

88
p espress.
Fl.
Ob.
Cor.igl.
Cl.
Cl.b.
Fg.
Cor. (F)
Tr. (F)
Vl.
Vla.
Vcl. e Ctb.
a 2
160
dim.
dim. espress.
Bassi

89

90

SECOND SUBORDINATE THEME—PART III

91

RETURN PRINCIPAL THEME

92

93

95

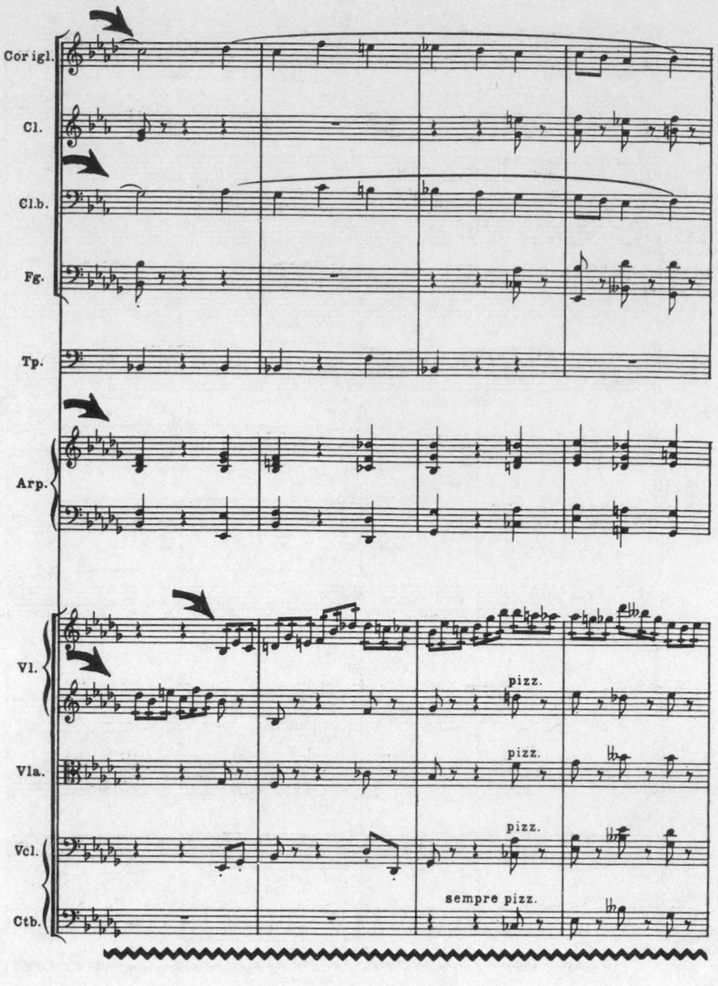

94

RETURN PRINCIPAL THEME—PART I

96

RETURN PRINCIPAL THEME—PART II

Fl.
Ob.
Cor. igl.
Cl.
Cl. b.
Fg.
Cor. (F)
Tr. (F)
Arp.
Vl.
Vla.
Vcl. e Ctb.
Bassi
cresc.
dim.
f
pp
p

CODA
220
poco rall.
Poco più lento
rall.
espress.
Fl.
Cor. igl.
Cl.
Cl. b.
Fg.
Cor. (F)
Vl.
Vla.
Vcl. e Ctb.
Vcl.
Ctb.
pp
CODA—SECTION 1
CODA—SECTION 2
CODA—SECTION 3

Cor. igl.
Cl. b.
Cor. (F)
Tp.
Arp.
Vl.
Vla.
Vcl. e Ctb.
pp

Poco piu lento
280
rall.
Fl.
Ob.
Cor. igl.
Cl.
Cl. b.
Fg.
Cor. (F)
Vl.
Vla.
Vcl.
Ctb.
pp

101

102

103

104

CODA—SECTION 4

105
Fl.
Ob.
Cor. igl.
Cl.
Cl. b.
Fg.
Cor. (F)
Tr. (F)
Tp.
Arp.
Vl.
Vla.
Vcl.
Ctb.
poco rall.
molto cresc.
molto sosten.
260

107
Cor. igl.
Cl.
Cl. b.
Fg.
Vl.
Vla.
Vcl.
Ctb.
PART I
cantabile
cresc.
dim.
mf espress.
PRINCIPAL THEME—PART II, 1st PERIOD

106
III
Allegro non troppo
EXPOSITION
2 Flauti
2 Oboi
Corno inglese
2 Clarinetti in B
Clarinetto basso in B
2 Fagotti
4 Corni in F
2 Trombe in F
Cornet à pist. I II in A
3 Tromboni III e Tuba
Timpani
Arpa
Violino I
Violino II
Viola
Violoncello
Contrabasso
dolce cantabile
INTRODUCTION
PRINCIPAL THEME—

108
Fl.
Ob.
Cor. igl.
Cl.
Cl. b.
Fg.
Cor. (F)
Tr. (F)
C. à p. (A)
Trb. e Tb.
Vl.
Vla.
Vcl.
Ctb.
f espress.
dim.
cresc.
unis.
PRINCIPAL THEME—PART II, 2nd PERIOD

109
Fl.
Ob.
Cor.igl.
Cl.
Cl.b.
Fg.
Cor. (F)
Tr. (F)
C. à p. (A)
Trb. e Tb.
Tp.
f cresc.
Vl.
Vla.
Vcl.
Ctb.
VARIATION PRINCIPAL THEME—PART I

110
40
Fl.
Ob.
Cor.igl.
Cl.
Cl.b.
Fg.
Cor. (F)
Tr. (F)
C. à p. (A)
Trb. e Tb.
Tp.
Vl.
Vla.
Vcl.
Ctb.

111
50
Fl.
Ob.
Cl.
Cl.b.
Fg.
p espress. e marcato
Vl.
Vla.
Vcl.
VARIATION PRINCIPAL THEME—PART II,
Cor. igl.
molto cresc.
1st PERIOD
VARIATION PRINCI-

112
60
Fl.
Ob.
Cor.igl.
Cl.
Cl.b.
Fg.
Cor. (F)
Tr. (F)
C. à p. (A)
Trb. e Tb.
Tp.
p molto cresc.
A muta in As
Vl.
Vla.
Vcl.
Ctb.
PAL THEME—PART II, 2nd PERIOD
BRIDGE PASSAGE

SUBORDINATE THEME—

PART I

SUBORDINATE

THEME—PART II

Ob.
Cor. igl.
Cl.
Cl. b.
Fg.
Cor. (F)
C. a p. (A)
Vl. II.
Vla.
Vcl.
Ctb.
unis.
molto legato
CODETTA—PART I
Vcl. e Ctb.
poco cresc.
molto dim.
espress.
menop
molto cresc.
Fl.
Arp.
Vl.
118
120
dim.
Tempo stretto come avanti
pp espr.
div.
CODETTA—PART II

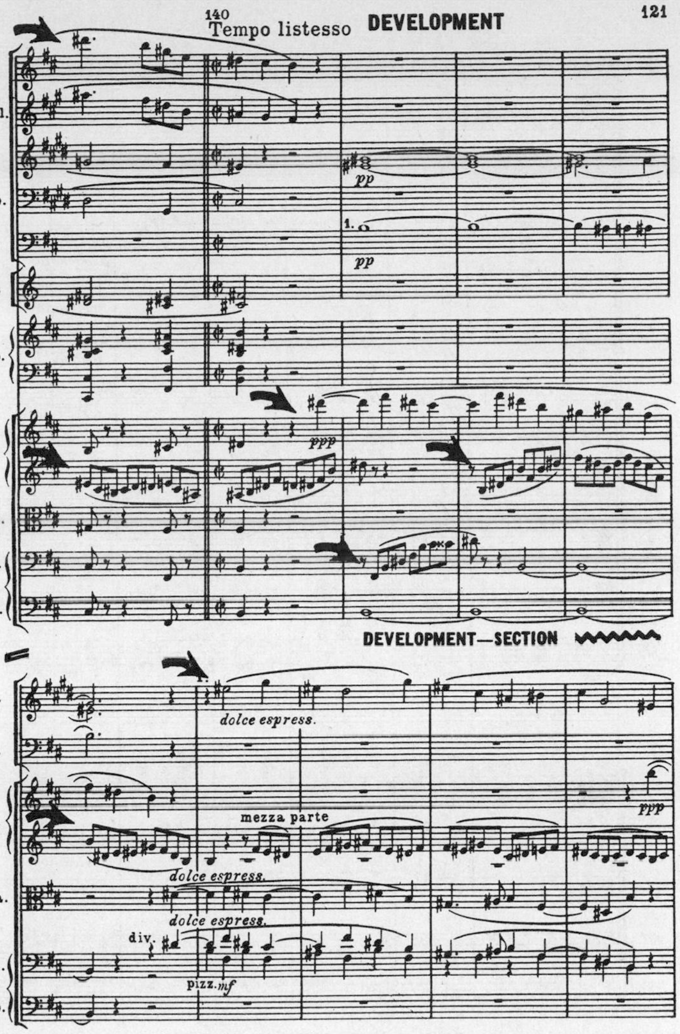
140
Tempo listesso
DEVELOPMENT
Fl.
Cor.igl.
Cl.
Cl.b.
Fg.
Cor. (F)
Arp.
Vl.
Vla.
Vcl.
Ctb.
pp
ppp
DEVELOPMENT—SECTION
dolce espress.
mezza parte
div.
pizz. mf

160
Fl.
Ob.
Cor.igl.
Cl.
Cl.b.
Fg.
Cor. (F)
Vl.
Vla.
Vcl. e Ctb.
Bassi
pp
cresc.
a 2
p
espress.

150
Fl.
Ob.
Cl.
Cl.b.
Cor. (F)
Vl.
Vla.
Vcl.
Ctb.
dolce espress
pp
tutti
espress.
unis
arco
ppp
div.
pizz mf
Vl. I.
unis.

170
a 2
Fl.
Ob.
Cor.igl.
Cl.
Cl.b.
Fg.
Cor. (F)
Tr. (F)
Tb.
Vl.
Vla.
Vcl.
Ctb.
f
cresc.
mf

Fl.
Ob.
Cor.igl.
Cl.
Cl.b.
Fg.
Cor. (F)
Tr. (F)
C. à p. (A)
III.Trb. e Tb.
Vl.
Vla.
Vcl.
Ctb.
a 2
ff

180
Fl.
Ob.
Cor.igl.
Cl.
Cl.b.
Fg.
Cor. (F)
Tr. (F)
C. à p. (A)
III.Trb. e Tb.
Tp.
Vl.
Vla.
Vcl.
Ctb.
mf
cresc.
trem.

190
Fl.
Ob.
Cor.igl.
Cl.
Cl.b.
Fg.
Cor. (F)
Tr. (F)
C. à p. (A)
Trb. e Tb.
Tp.
Vl.
Vla.
Vcl.
Ctb.
a 2
ff
sostenuto
As muta in G
DEVELOPMENT—SECTION 2

Fl.
Ob.
Cor.igl.
Cl.
Cl.b.
Fg.
Cor. (F)
Tr. (F)
C. à p. (A)
Trb. e Tb.
Vl.
Vla.
Vcl.
Ctb.
3

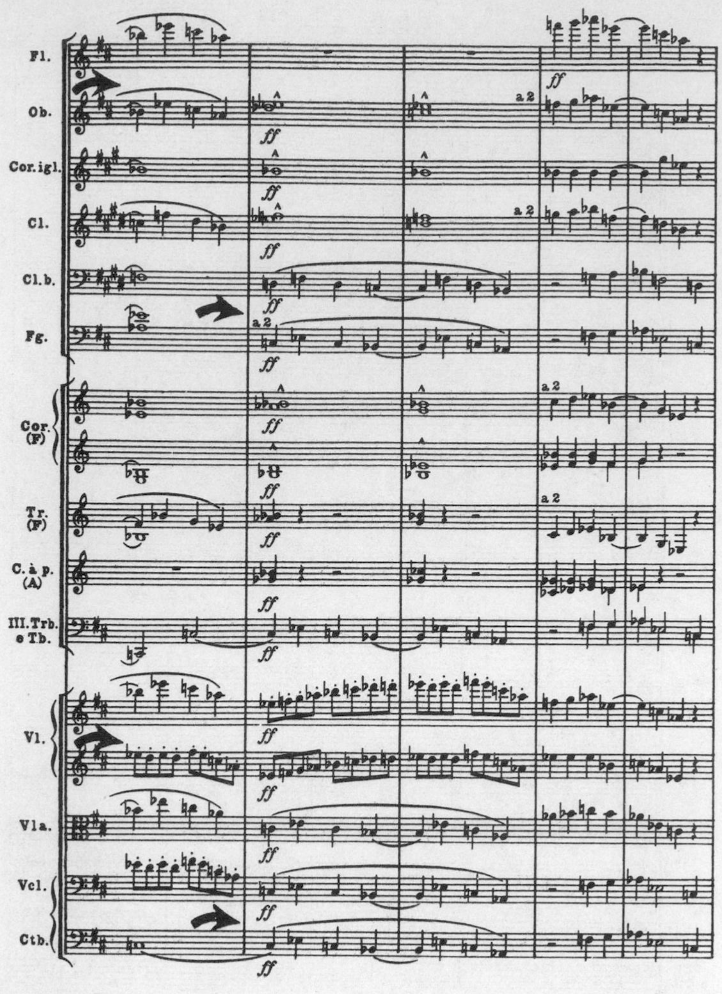

DEVELOPMENT—SECTION 3

DEVELOPMENT—SECTION 4

RETURNING PASSAGE (RETRAN

133
250
a 2
Fl.
Ob.
Cor igl.
Cl.
Cl.b.
Fg.
Cor. (F)
III Trb. e Tb.
Tb.
Tp.
Vl.
Vla.
Vcl.
Ctb.
poco a poco cresc.
SITION)

134
a 2
Fl.
Ob.
Cor igl.
Cl.
Cl.b.
Fg.
Cor. (F)
III Trb. e Tb.
Tp.
Vl
Vla.
Vcl.
Ctb.

135
260
Fl.
Ob.
Cor igl.
Cl.
Cl.b.
Fg.
Cór. (F)
Tr. (F)
C. à p. (A)
Trb. e Tb.
Tb.
Vl.
Vla.
Vcl.
Ctb.

136
a 2
Fl.
Ob.
Cor igl.
Cl.
Cl.b.
Fg.
Cor. (F)
Tr. (F)
C. à p. (A)
Trb. e Tb.
Tp.
Vl.
Vla.
Vcl. e Ctb.
cresc.

RECAPITULATION

RETURN PRINCIPAL THEME—PART I

THEME—PART II

RETURN PRINCIPAL

141
CODA
Tempo come avanti
300
Fl.
Ob.
Cor igl.
Cl.
Cl.b.
Fg.
Cor. (F)
Tr. (F)
C. à p. (A)
Trb. e Tb.
Tp.
Vl.
Vla.
Vcl.
Ctb.
ff sempre
a 2
ff
CODA—SECTION I
142
143
a 2
144
310

145

146

CODA—SECTION 2

147

CODA—SECTION 3

148

CODA—SECTION 4

Cl.b.
C.à p. (A)
Trb. e Tb.
Tp.
Arp.
Vl.
Vla.
Vcl. e Ctb.
a 2
Tb.
ppp
pp espress.
360
double corde

Fl.
Ob.
Cor.igl.
Cl.
Cl.b.
Fg.
Cor. (F)
C.à p. (A)
Trb. e Tb.
Tp.
Arp.
Vl.
Vla.
Vcl. e Ctb.
a 2
370
molto cresc.
dim.
cresc.
sostenuto

Cl.b.
C.à p. (A)
Trb. e Tb.
Tp.
Arp.
Vl.
Vla.
Vcl. e Ctb.
a 2
Tb.
380
div.

Fl.
Ob.
Cor.igl.
Cl.
Cl.b.
Fg.
Cor. (F)
C.à p. (A)
Tb.
Vl.
Vla
Vcl.
Ctb.
a 2
molto cresc.
dim.
cresc.

CODA—SECTION 5

420
Fl.
Ob.
Cor.igl.
Cl.
Cl.b.
Fg.
Cor. (F)
Tr. (F)
C.à p. (A)
Trb. e Tb.
a 2
Tp.
Vl.
Vla.
Vcl. e Ctb.
Bassi

Fl.
Ob.
Cor.igl.
Cl.
Cl.b.
Fg.
Cor. (F)
Tr. (F)
C.a p. (A)
Trb. e Tb.
Tp.
ff
Vl.
Vla.
Vcl. e Ctb.

430
Fl.
Ob.
Cor.igl.
Cl.
Cl.b.
Fg.
Cor. (F)
Tr. (F)
C.à p. (A)
Trb. e Tb.
a 2
Tp.
Vl.
Vla.
Vcl. e Ctb.

Fl.
Ob.
Cor.igl.
Cl.
Cl.b.
Fg.
Cor. (F)
Tr. (F)
C.à p. (A)
a 2
Trb. e Tb.
Tp.
Vl.
Vla.
Vcl.
Ctb.

SYMPHONY No. 7 IN E MAJOR — *ANTON BRUCKNER*

MOVEMENTS:

I. *Allegro moderato*

II. *Sehr feierlich und langsam*

III. *Scherzo—Sehr schnell*

IV. *Bewegt, doch nicht schnell*

Symphony No. 7 is scored for the following instruments:

2 Flöten (Flutes)	*Fl.*	2 Pauken (Timpani)	*Pk.*
2 Oboen (Oboes)	*Ob.*	Triangel (Triangle)	*Trgl.*
2 Klarinetten (Clarinets)	*Kl.*	Becken (Cymbals)	*Beck.*
2 Fagotte (Bassoons)	*Fg.*	1. Violinen (1st Violins)	*Vl.*
4 Hörner (Horns)	*Hr.*	2. Violinen (2nd Violins)	*Vl.*
3 Trompeten (Trumpets)	*Tr.*	Bratschen (Violas)	*Br.*
3 Posaunen (Trombones)	*Pos.*	Violoncelle (Violoncellos)	*Vc.*
4 Tuben (Tubas)	*Tb.*	Kontrabässe (Double Basses)	*Kb.*

Each instrument is listed above under its name as printed on the first page of the score; its English equivalent, and the abbreviation used on succeeding pages.

Bruckner wrote this symphony while his fifth and sixth symphonies were still unperformed. It was begun in September 1881 and completed in September 1883. The first performance was given in Leipzig on December 30, 1884 at a Wagner memorial concert conducted by Bruckner's pupil, Arthur Nikisch, and proved to be a signal triumph for the composer. It was again performed in Munich under Hermann Levi on March 10, 1885 with equal success. At the present time, it is almost as much played as the Fourth Symphony, in spite of the fact that it requires four tubas.

The *Adagio* is presumed to have been written with a premonition on the part of Bruckner that the death of his beloved master, Richard Wagner, was soon to take place. This *Adagio* was completed in October 1882, and Wagner died on February 13, 1883. In a letter written to Felix Mottl in 1885 regarding the first performance of this symphony at Carlsruhe, Bruckner writes: "At one time I came home and was very sad; I thought to myself, it is impossible that the Master can live for a long time, and then the *Adagio* in C sharp minor came into my head".

There are two recordings of this symphony: one by the Minneapolis Symphony Orchestra under the direction of Eugene Ormandy, and another by the Berlin Philharmonic Orchestra under the baton of Jascha Horenstein.

Symphony No. 7

EXPOSITION I.

Allegro moderato. (M. 𝅗𝅥 = 58)

Anton Bruckner

5
50
Pos.
Tb.
Vl.
Br.
Vc.
Kb.
pp
dim.
Ruhig. (♩=108)
Ob.
Kl.
Hr. (F)
Tr. (F)
I. II.
I.
mf
FIRST SUBORDINATE THEME

6
60
Ob.
Kl.
Hr. (F)
Tr. (F)
Vl.
Br.
Vc. Kb.
dim.
cresc.
mf
Fl.
Pos.
pp
p

7
70
Fl.
Kl.
Hr. (F)
Pos.
Vl.
Br.
Vc. Kb.
p ausdrucksvoll
cresc.
p poco a poco cresc.
Tb.
cresc. sempre

8
80
Ob.
Kl.
Hr.
Pos.
Tb
Vl.
Br.
Vc.
Kb
dim.
mf
pp

9
90
poco a poco cresc.
pizz.
10
100
zu 2
immer hervortretend
arco
div.
INVERSION FIRST SUBOR —
DINATE THEME
11
110
zu 2
p poco a poco cresc.
pp poco a poco cresc.
poco a poco cresc.
12
etwas belebend
zu 2
a poco cresc.
poco cresc.

13
zu 2
120
rit.
Fl.
Ob.
Kl.
Fg.
Hr. (F)
Tr. (F)
Pos.
Tb.
Vl.
Br.
Vc.
Kb.

15
zu 2
Kl.
Fg.
Hr. (F)
Vl.
Br.
Vc. Kb.
p dim.
Fl.
Ob.

14
Ruhig. (𝅗𝅥 = 96)
pp a tempo
p a tempo
Fl.
Ob.
Kl.
Fg.
Vl.
Br.
Vc. Kb.
SECOND SUBORDINATE THEME
130
cresc.
Hr. (F)
Tb.
I. II.

16
zu 2
140
cresc. sempre
Fl.
Ob
Kl.
Fg.
Hr. (F)
Tr. (F)
Pos.
Vl.
Br.
Vc. Kb.

17

Fl.
Ob.
Kl.
Fg.
Hr. (F)
Tr. (F)
Pos.
Tb.
Vl.
Br.
Vc. Kb.
zu2
ff marc.
f
ff

19

Kl.
Fg.
Hr. (F)
Tr. (F)
Pos.
Tb.
Vl.
Br.
Vc. Kb.
ff dim.
p
dim.
pp
150
hervortretend

18

Fl.
Ob.
Kl.
Fg.
Hr. (F)
Tr. (F)
Pos.
Tb.
Vl.
Br.
Vc. Kb.
zu2
cresc.
ff
fff

20

Hr. (F)
Vl.
Br.
Vc. Kb.
Kl.
I.
III.
div.
p
pp
pp immer etwas hervortretend
pp hervortretend
pizz.
CODETTA
160
dim.

DEVELOPMENT
21
Ruhig.
170
zu2
DEVELOPMENT—SECTION 1
cresc.
180
ritard.
22
a tempo
190
div.
arco
DEVELOPMENT—SECTION 2
immer hervortretend
200
23
mf cresc.
am besten Tuben
Pos.
dim.
f cresc.
hervortretend
div.
24
Belebend.
pp poco a poco cresc.
mf poco cresc.
Ruhig.
220
DEVELOPMENT—SECTION 3

25
Kl.
Vl.
Br.
Vo. Kb.
Fl.
I.II.
dim.
dolce
ppp
230

27
zu 2
Fl.
Ob.
Kl.
Fg.
Hr. (F)
Tr. (F)
Pos.
Tb.
Vl.
Br.
Vo. Kb.

26
Tempo I.
zu 2
240
Fl.
Ob.
Kl.
Fg.
Hr. (F)
Tr. (F)
Pos.
Tb.
Vl.
div
Br.
Vo. Kb.
DEVELOPMENT—SECTION 4

28
250
Ob.
Kl.
Fg.
Hr. (F)
poco a poco cresc.
Vl.
Br.
Vo.
Kb.
260
Fl.
III. IV.
Tr. (F)
poco cresc.
dim.

29
270
Ob.
Kl.
Fg.
Hr. (F)
Vl.
Br.
Vo.
Kb.
Fl.
Tr. (F)
zu 2
poco a poco cresc.
div.
RETURNING PASSAGE (RETRANSITION)

30
280
Ob.
Kl.
Fg.
Tr. (F)
Vl.
Br.
Vo.
Fl.
Hr. (F)
zu 2
p zart
hervortretend
RECAPITULATION
RETURN PRINCIPAL THEME

31
290
300
Fl.
Ob.
Kl.
Hr. (F)
Tr. (F)
Vl.
Br.
Vo.
zu 2
poco a poco cresc.
dim. sempre

32
310
Fl.
Kl.
Hr. (F)
Vl.
Br.
Vo.
Kb.
zu 2
div.
ppp sempre

33
320
simile
Fl.
Ob.
Kl.
Fg.
Vl.
Br.
Hr. (F)
Tr. (F)
Vc. Kb.
pizz.
RETURN FIRST SUBORDINATE THEME
RETURN INVER —

34
330
Fl.
Kl.
Hr. (F)
Vl.
Br.
Vc. Kb.
Ob.
cresc.
dim.
pizz.
arco
zu 2 sempre
SION FIRST SUBORDINATE THEME

35
zu 2
poco a poco
divisi
340
cresc.
immer breiter
Fl.
Ob.
Kl.
Fg.
Hr. (F)
Vl.
Br.
Vc. Kb.

36
zu 2
divisi
Fl.
Ob.
Kl.
Fg.
Hr. (F)
Tr. (F)
Pos.
Tb.
Vl.
Br.
Vc. Kb.

37

zu 2
Fl.
Ob.
Kl.
Fg.
Hr. (F)
Tr. (F)
Pos.
Tb.
Vl.
Br.
Vo. Kb.

39

a tempo
zu 2
Kl.
I. II.
Hr. (F)
Pos.
Vl.
Br.
Vo.
Kb.
poco
a
cresc.
Ob.
mf cresc.
sempre
div.

38

350
etwas gedehnt
zu 2
Fl.
Ob.
Kl.
Hr. (F)
Tr. (F)
Pos.
Tb.
Vl.
Br.
Vo.
Kb.
dim.
pp poco
p poco
a
divisi

40

breiter
360
zu 2
Ob.
Kl.
Hr. (F)
Pos.
Vl.
Br.
Vo.
Kb.
ff

41
ruhig
Fl.
Ob.
Kl.
Hr. (F)
Pos.
Vl.
Br.
Vc.
Kb.
zu 2
dim.
pp
RETURN SECOND SUBOR —
43
370
Fg.
Tr. (F)
Vc. Kb.
42
— DINATE THEME
44
Tb.
hervortretend

45

Fl.
Ob.
Kl.
Fg.
Hr. (F)
Vl.
Br.
Vc. Kb.
zu 2
pp poco a
hervortretend
380
poco
cresc.
p cresc.

47

390
Fl.
Ob.
Kl.
Fg.
Hr. (F)
Tr. (F)
Pos.
Tb.
Vl.
Br.
Vc. Kb.
zu 2
pp
dim.
ppp

46

Fl.
Ob.
Kl.
Fg.
Hr. (F)
Tr. (F)
Pos.
Tb.
Vl.
Br.
Vc. Kb.
zu 2
ff
fff
ff marc. sempre
f marc. sempre

48

Sehr feierlich.
400
Fl.
Ob.
Kl.
Pk.
Vl.
Br.
Vc.
Kb.
zu 2
p poco a poco cresc.
pp poco a poco cresc.
cresc. sempre
mf poco a
poco cresc.
ff poco a poco dim.
poco a poco dim.

CODA
49
Sehr ruhig;
410
zu 2
I.
dim. sempre
Fl.
Ob.
Kl.
Hr. (F)
Pos.
Tb.
Pk.
Vl.
Br.
Vc.
Kb.
divisi
51
420
mf poco a poco cresc.
marc. sempre
Fg.
Tr. (F)
50
nach und nach etwas schneller
II.
III.
52
cresc.
sempre cresc.
marc.

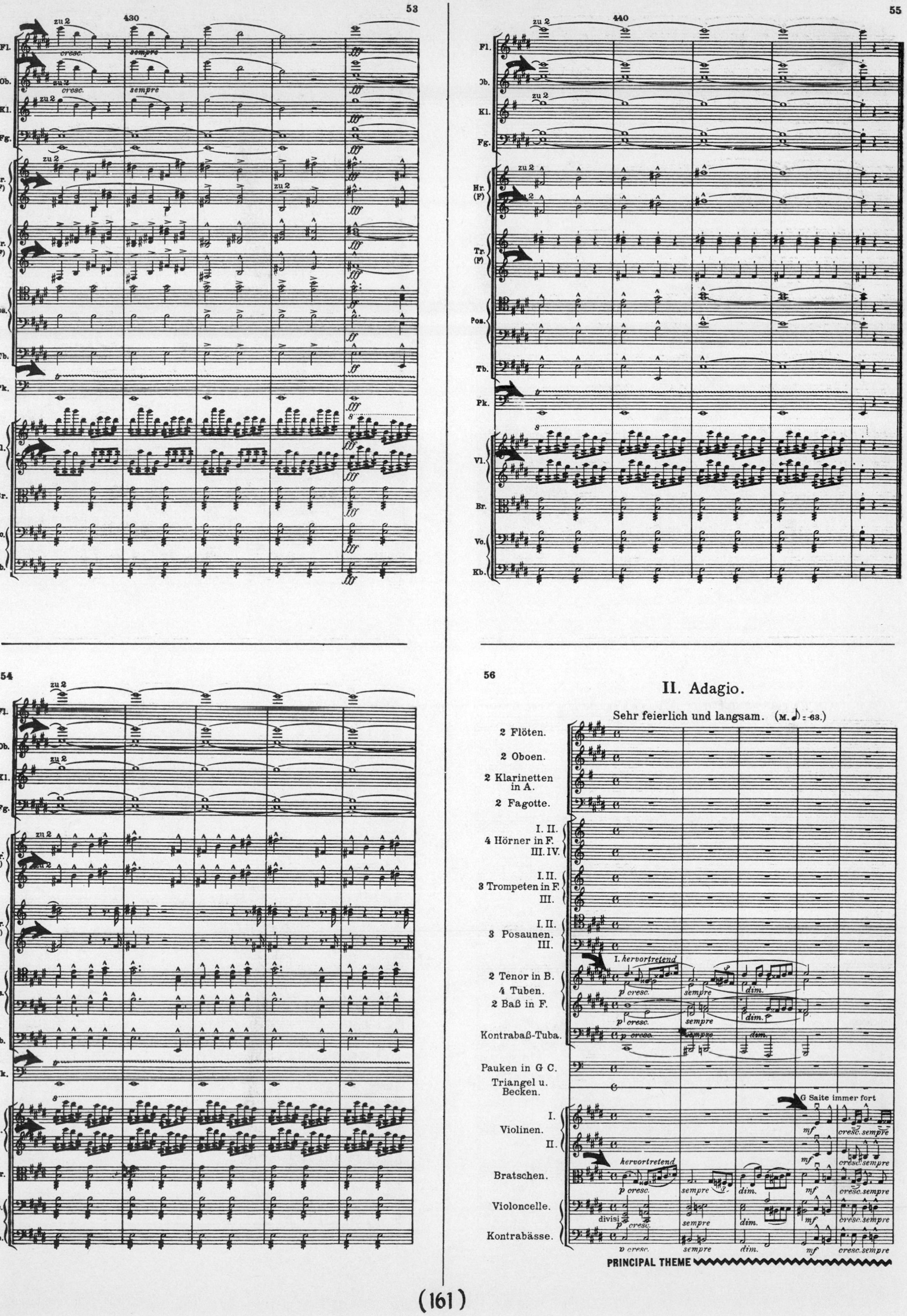
53
430
55
440
54
56
II. Adagio.
Sehr feierlich und langsam. (M. ♪ = 63.)
2 Flöten.
2 Oboen.
2 Klarinetten in A.
2 Fagotte.
I. II. 4 Hörner in F. III. IV.
I. II. 3 Trompeten in F. III.
I. II. 3 Posaunen. III.
2 Tenor in B. 4 Tuben. 2 Baß in F.
Kontrabaß-Tuba.
Pauken in G C.
Triangel u. Becken.
I. Violinen. II.
Bratschen.
Violoncelle.
Kontrabässe.
I. hervortretend
hervortretend
G Saite immer fort
divisi
PRINCIPAL THEME
Fl.
Ob.
Kl.
Fg.
Hr. (F)
Tr. (F)
Pos.
Tb.
Pk.
Vl.
Br.
Vc.
Kb.
zu 2
cresc.
sempre
dim.

10
Hr. (F)
Pos.
Vl.
Br.
Vc. Kb.
Ob.
Kl.
III.IV.
sehr markiert
zart
zogen
hervortretend
divisi
p dim.
cresc.
pp
mf

zu 2
Fl.
Ob.
Kl.
Fg.
Hr. (F)
Tr. (F)
Pos.
(B) Tb. (F)
Ktb.
Vl.
Br.
Vc.
Kb.
p cresc.
cresc.
ff

zu 2
20
Fl.
Ob.
Kl.
Fg.
Hr. (F)
Vl.
Br.
Vc.
Kb.
cresc.
dim.
pp

30
zu 2
I.
I.II.
Fl.
Ob.
Kl.
Fg.
Hr. (F)
Tr. (F)
Pos.
(B) Tb. (F)
Ktb.
Vl.
Br.
Vc.
Kb.
sempre dim.
pp

61

Moderato. (M. ♪ = 92.)
I.
Hr. (F)
B) Tb. (F)
Ktb.
Vl.
Br.
Vo.
Kb.
dim.
p
cresc.
SUBORDINATE THEME
40 II.
Kl.
Fg.
SUBORDINATE THEME

62

hervortretend
Vl.
Br.
Vo.
Kb.
divisi
p
cresc. sempre
50
Hr. (F)
IV.
f
f cresc.
dim.

63

I.
Fl.
Kl.
II.
Fg.
Hr. (F)
III. IV.
Vl.
Br.
Vo.
Kb.
pp
p
poco cresc.
cresc.
dim.
60

64

Vl.
Br.
Vo.
Kb.
pp
p
Fg.
Hr. (F)
pp cresc.
cresc.

65
70
Hr. (F)
Vl.
Br.
Vc.
Kb.
sehr ruhig
cresc.
sempre
mf
dim.
f
Tempo I.
zu 2
Tr. (F)
(B) Tb. (F)
Ktb.
hervortretend
p cresc.
pp
FIRST RETURN PRINCIPAL THEME

66
80
Kl.
Fg.
zu 2
p cresc.
Hr. (F)
Tr. (F)
Pos.
p dim.
(B) Tb. (F)
Ktb.
G Saite
sehr markiert
Vl.
Br.
Vc.
Kb.
mf
cresc.
sempre
divisi

67
90
Fl.
Ob.
Kl.
Fg.
zu 2
p poco a poco cresc.
mf cresc.
Hr. (F)
Tr. (F)
I.
I. marc.
Vl.
Br.
Vc.
Kb.

68
Fl.
Ob.
Kl.
Hr (F)
Tr. (F)
Vl.
Br.
Vc. Kb.
zu 2
I.
p cresc.
sempre
dim.
Fg.
mf poco a poco cresc.

Fl.
Ob.
Kl.
Fg.
Hr. (F)
Tr. (F)
Vl.
Br.
Vc. Kb.
zu 2
f cresc.
hervortretend
div.
dim.
pp

Fl.
Vl.
Br.
Vc. Kb.
Kl.
Fg.
Hr. (F)
zu 2
div.
110
pp
poco a poco cresc.
pp sempre

Fl.
Kl.
Fg.
Hr. (F)
Vl.
Br.
Vc. Kb.
Ob.
cresc.
G Saite
mf
zu 2
sehr markiert
p cresc.

Fl.
Ob.
Kl.
Fg.
Hr. (F)
Pos.
Vl.
Br.
Vc.
120
zu 2
mf
p cresc.
cresc.

zu 2
f cresc.
ff

ritard.
Moderato.
dim.
p hervortr.
cresc.
RETURN SUBORDINATE THEME

130

140
G Saite
hervortretend
dim.
cresc.

77
Ob.
Kl.
Hr. (F)
Vl.
Br.
Vo.
pp
mf
cresc.
dim.
150
Fg.
Kb.
poco rit.

78
Kl.
Fg.
Hr. (F)
Vl.
Br.
Vo.
Kb.
immer ruhiger
rit.
Tempo I.
Sehr langsam.
hervortretend
cresc.
(B) Tb. (F)
Ktb.
In gleicher Stärke, ohne Anschwellung
div.
SECOND RETURN PRINCIPAL THEME

79
160
(B) Tb. (F)
Ktb.
Vl.
Br.
Vo.
Kb.
dim.
G Saite
mf
cresc.
sehr markiert

80
Hr (F)
Pos.
(B) Tb. (F)
Ktb.
Vl.
Br.
Vo.
Kb.
p dim.
I. hervortretend
pp
hervortretend
cresc.

81

Pos.
(B) Tb. (F)
Ktb.
Vl.
Br.
Vc.
Kb.
cresc.
p
170
Hr. (F)
zu 2
mf
I.
II.

82

Fl.
Ob.
Kl.
Fg.
Hr. (F)
Tr. (F)
Pos.
(B) Tb. (F)
Vl.
Br.
Vc.
Kb.
zu 2
cresc.
mf
f
ff
semp. portamento
gestrichen

83

Fl.
Ob.
Kl.
Fg.
Hr. (F)
Tr. (F)
Pos.
Vl.
Br.
Vc. Kb.
zu 2

84

Fl.
Ob.
Kl.
Fg.
Hr. (F)
Tr. (F)
Pos.
(B) Tb. (F)
Ktb.
Vl.
Br.
Vc. Kb.
zu 2
cresc.
III.
ff
f

85

Fl.
Ob.
Kl.
Fg.
Hr. (F)
Tr. (F)
Pos.
(B) Tb. (F)
Ktb.
Pk.
Trgl. Beck.
Vl.
Br.
Vo. Kb.
zu 2
II. hervortretend
ausklingen lassen
(G)

86

Fl.
Ob.
Kl.
Fg.
Hr. (F)
Tr. (F)
Pos.
(B) Tb. (F)
Ktb.
Pk.
Vl.
Br.
Vo. Kb.
zu 2
180

87

CODA
Fl.
Ob.
Kl.
Fg.
Hr. (F)
Tr. (F)
Pos.
(B) Tb. (F)
Ktb.
Pk.
Vl.
Br.
Vo. Kb.
zu 2
dim.
pizz.

88

190
sehr ausdrucksvoll
Hr. (F)
(B) Tb. (F)
Ktb.
Fl.
Vl.
Br.
Vo. Kb.
I. II.
zu 2
cresc.
dim.
rfz
pizz.

89
200
Fl.
Ob.
Kl.
Vl.
Br.
Vc. Kb.
cresc.
mf recht gesangvoll
dim.
pizz.
p dim. sempre
pp dim.

III. Scherzo.
91
PRINCIPAL SECTION
Sehr schnell. (M.𝅗𝅥. = 80.)
2 Flöten.
2 Oboen.
2 Klarinetten in A.
2 Fagotte.
I. II. 4 Hörner in F. III. IV.
I. II. 3 Trompeten in F. III.
I. II. 3 Posaunen. III.
Baßtuba.
Pauken. in C.G.A.
I. Violinen. II.
Bratschen.
Violoncelle.
Kontrabässe.
p hervortretend
INTRODUCTION
PRINCIPAL THEME—PART I

90
210
Fl.
Hr (F)
(B) Tb. (F)
Ktb.
Vl.
Br.
Vc.
Kb.
zu 2
cresc.
arco
div.
dim.
pizz.

92
10
Kl.
Tr. (F)
Vl.
Br.
Vc. Kb.
p hervortretend
dim.
20
Ob.
Hr. (F)
cresc.
PRINCIPAL THEME—PART II

93

95

94

PRINCIPAL THEME—PART III

96

PRINCIPAL THEME—PART IV

Fl.
Ob.
Kl.
Fg.
Hr. (F)
Tr. (F)
Pos.
Tb.
Pk.
Vl.
Br.
Vo. Kb.
zu 2
70

Fl.
Ob.
Kl.
Fg.
Hr. (F)
Tr. (F)
Pos.
Tb.
Pk.
Vl.
Br.
Vo. Kb.
zu 2

Fl.
Ob.
Kl.
Fg.
Hr. (F)
Tr. (F)
Pos.
Tb.
Pk.
Vl.
Br.
Vo. Kb.
zu 2
80

90
Kl.
Pk.
G nach E tief
Vl.
Br.
Vo.
Kb.
zu 2
VARIATION PRINCIPAL THEME—PART II
100
Fl.

101
110
120
zu 2
Fl.
Ob.
Kl.
Hr
(F)
Tr.
(F)
Vl.
Br.
Vc.
cresc.
poco
a
poco
ppp
mf
f

102
Etwas ruhiger.
130
zu 2
Fl.
Ob.
Kl.
Fg.
Hr.
(F)
Tr.
(F)
Vl.
Br.
Vc.
p poco
a
poco
cresc.
f cresc.
mf

103
140
zu 2
Ob.
Kl.
Fg.
Hr.
(F)
Pos.
Tb.
Vl.
Br.
Vc.
Kb.
III.
III. IV.
cresc.
p cresc.
pp
ff

104
150
160
Fl.
Ob.
Kl.
Fg.
Hr.
(F)
Vl.
Br.
Vc.
Kb.
p hervortretend
pizz.
pp
VARIATION
PRINCIPAL THEME—PART I

105
zu 2
Fl.
Ob.
Kl.
Hr. (F)
Tr. (F)
Vl.
Br.
Vo. Kb.
poco a poco cresc.
sempre
170
divisi
arco

107
zu 2
Fl.
Ob.
Kl.
Fg.
Hr. (F)
Tr. (F)
Pk.
Vl.
Br.
Vo. Kb.
RETURN PRINCIPAL THEME—PART I
190

106
zu 2
180
Fl.
Ob.
Kl.
Fg.
Hr. (F)
Tr. (F)
Pos.
Tb.
Pk.
Vl.
Br.
Vo. Kb.

108
200
Fl.
Ob.
Kl.
Hr. (F)
Vl.
Br.
Vo. Kb.
H
210
zu 2
Fg.
Tr. (F)
RETURN PRINCIPAL THEME-

PART II

RETURN PRINCIPAL THEME—PART III

RETURN PRINCIPAL THEME—PART IV

zu 2
250
Fl.
Ob.
Kl.
Fg.
Hr. (F)
Tr. (F)
Pos.
Tb.
Pk.
Vl.
Br.
Vc. Kb.

zu 2
Fl.
Ob.
Kl.
Fg.
Hr. (F)
Tr. (F)
Pos.
Tb.
Pk.
Vl.
Br.
Vc. Kb.

260
zu 2
270
Fl.
Ob.
Kl.
Fg.
Hr. (F)
Tr. (F)
Pos.
Tb.
Pk.
Vl.
Br.
Vc. Kb.

TRIO Etwas langsamer M. ♩. 42
E nach G
10
gesangvoll
cresc. sempre
INTRODUCTION
SUBORDINATE THEME—PART I
20
p cresc. sempre
dim.
30
f cresc.
pp poco a poco cresc.
Pk.
Vl.
Br.
Vc.
Kb.
Hr. (F)
Tr. (F)

SUBORDINATE THEME—PART II

SUBORDINATE THEME—PART III

BRIDGE PASSAGE

RETURN SUBORDINATE THEME—PART I

121
Fl.
Ob.
Kl.
Hr. (F)
Tr. (F)
Pos.
Tb.
Vl.
Br.
Vc.
Kb.
zu 2
p cresc. sempre
dim.
f

122
110
Fl.
Ob.
Kl.
Hr. (F)
Tr. (F)
Pos.
Tb.
Vl.
Br.
Vc.
Kb.
zu 2
I.
cresc. sempre
ff
dim.

123
120
130
Fl.
Ob.
Kl.
Hr. (F)
Pk.
Vl.
Br.
Vc.
Kb.
zu 2
I.
pp
ppp
cresc.
dim.
Scherzo da Capo

124
EXPOSITION
IV. Finale.
Bewegt, doch nicht schnell M. 𝅗𝅥 = 63
2 Flöten.
2 Oboen.
2 Klarinetten in A.
2 Fagotte.
4 Hörner in F. I. II. III. IV.
3 Trompeten in F. I. II. III.
3 Posaunen. I. II. III.
2 Tenor in B. 4 Tuben. 2 Baß in F.
Kontrabaß-Tuba.
Pauken C u. E tief.
Violinen. I. II.
Bratschen.
Violoncelle.
Kontrabässe.
Spitze
divisi
pp
poco a poco cresc.
PRINCIPAL THEME

125
riten.
a tempo
Fl.
Ob.
Vl.
Br.
Vo.
Kb.
dim. sempre
Spitze
Kl.
zu 2
Hr. (F)
Tr. (F)
marc.
mf poco a poco cresc.

126
a tempo
Fl.
Kl.
zu 2
Hr. (F)
Tr. (F)
Vl.
Br.
Vo.
Kb.
dim. mf
poco a poco
cresc.
III. IV.

127
Hr. (F)
zu 2
cresc.
dim.
Vl.
Br.
Vo.
Kb.
p poco a poco cresc.
pizz.
SUBORDINATE THEME
(B) Tb. (F)
cresc.

128
Ob.
Kl.
zu 2
Hr. (F)
Pk.
dim. sempre
cresc.
Fl.
poco a poco dim.
III.
Vl.
Br.
Vo.
Kb.
pp poco a

DEVELOPMENT

129

130

CODETTA

131

DEVELOPMENT—SECTION I

132

133
Fl.
Ob.
Kl.
Fg.
Hr. (F)
Tr. (F)
Pos.
(B) Tb. (F)
Ktb.
Vl.
Br.
Vc. Kb.
zu 2
marc. sempre

134
Tempo I.
110
Fl.
Ob.
Kl.
Fg.
Hr. (F)
Tr. (F)
Pos.
(B) Tb. (F)
Ktb.
Vl.
Br.
Vc. Kb.
zu 2
fff marc.
ff marc.
marc.

135
I.
I. II.
Tr. (F)
Vl.
Br.
Vc. Kb.
div.
pp poco a poco cresc.
marc.
DEVELOPMENT—SECTION 2
120
Kl.
Hr. (F)
Spitze
130
DEVELOPMENT—SECTION 3

136
I
Kl.
Hr. (F)
Vl.
Br.
Vc. Kb.
Fl.
140
Pk.
dim. sempre
DEVELOPMENT—SEC-

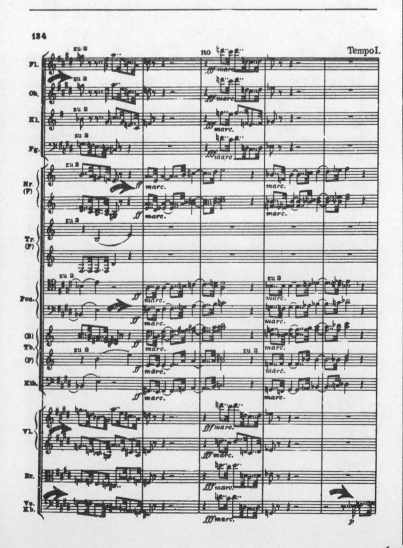

137
150
Fl.
Ob.
Kl.
(B)
Tb.
(F)
Pk.
ruhig
cresc.
TION 4
a tempo
160
Fg.
sempre
ruhig
pp

138
nur ruhig bewegt
(B)
Tb.
(F)
Pk.
Vl.
Br.
Vc.
Kb.
cresc.
Spitze
pizz.
ritard.
a tempo
170
Ob.
Kl.
streng im Zeitmaß
dim.
DEVELOPMENT—

139
Vl.
Spitze
Br.
180
Fl.
Ob.
Kl.
marc. sempre
poco
zu 2
immer hervortret.
Hr
(F)
dim. sempre
pizz. div.
SECTION 5
cresc.
Hr
(F)
Vl.
Br.

140
190
zu 2
Fl.
Ob.
Kl.
Fg.
Hr.
(F)
Tr.
(F)
Pos.
(B)
Tb.
(F)
Ktb.
Vl.
Br.
Vc.
Kb.
cresc.
sempre
ff
marc.
mf cresc.
cresc. sempre
cresc. sempre
sempre marc.

141
Fl.
Ob.
Kl.
Fg.
Hr. (F)
Tr. (F)
Pos.
(B) Tb. (F)
Ktb.
Vl.
Br.
Vc. Kb.

143
Fl.
Ob.
Kl.
Fg.
Hr. (F)
Tr. (F)
Pos.
(B) Tb. (F)
Ktb.
Vl.
Br.
Vc. Kb.

142
Breit und wuchtig
200
Fl.
Ob.
Kl.
Fg.
Hr. (F)
Tr. (F)
Pos.
(B) Tb. (F)
Ktb.
Vl.
Br.
Vc.
Kb.
RETURNING PASSAGE (RETRANSITION)

144
immer breiter
210
Fl.
Ob.
Kl.
Fg.
Hr. (F)
Tr. (F)
Pos.
(B) Tb. (F)
Ktb.
Vl.
Br.
Vc.
Kb.

RECAPITULATION
145
Tempo I 𝅗𝅥=52
Fl.
Ob.
Kl.
Fg.
Hr. (F)
Tr. (F)
Pos.
(B) Tb. (F)
Ktb.
Vl.
Br.
Vc. Kb.
pp poco a poco cresc.
cresc. sempre
pizz.
RETURN SUBORDINATE THEME

146
220
Ob.
Kl.
Hr. (F)
(B) Tb. (F)
Vl.
Br.
Vc. Kb.
Tr. (F)
Kb.
ppp
p cresc. sempre
pizz.
mf cresc.

147
230
Ob.
Kl.
Hr. (F)
Pk.
dim. sempre
240
dim.
pp poco a poco cresc.
arco
poco a poco cresc.
pizz.
Vl.
Br.

148
Tempo I
Fl.
Ob.
Kl.
Hr. (F)
Pk.
Vl.
Br.
Vc.
p marc.
poco a poco
cresc.
dim.
arco
pp poco a poco

a tempo
ritard.
dim
marc. sempre
poco a poco
zu 2
cresc.
marc.
mf
sempre
ff marc.
dim.
arco
Ob.
Kl.
Hr. (F)
Pos.
(B) Tb. (F)
Ktb.
Vl.
Br.
Vc.
Kb.

Breit.
zu 2
I.
cresc.
ff marc. sempre
Fl.
Ob.
Kl.
Fg.
Hr. (F)
Tr. (F)
Pos.
(B) Tb. (F)
Ktb.
Vl.
Br.
Vc.
Kb.

260
zu 2
marc. sempre
sempre
Fl.
Ob.
Kl.
Fg.
Hr. (F)
Tr. (F)
Pos.
(B) Tb. (F)
Ktb.
Vl.
Br.
Vc. Kb.

zu 2
ff
Fl.
Ob.
Kl.
Fg.
Hr. (F)
Tr. (F)
Pos.
(B) Tb. (F)
Ktb.
Vl.
Br.
Vc. Kb.

153
270
Fl.
Ob.
Kl.
Fg.
Hr. (F)
Tr. (F)
Pos.
(B) Tb. (F)
Ktb.
Vl.
Br.
Vo. Kb.
zu 2
ff marc.
ff marc. sempre
fff

154
Tempo I.
Fl.
Ob.
Kl.
Hr. (F)
Tr. (F)
Pos.
(B) Tb. (F)
Ktb.
Vl.
Br.
Vo. Kb.
zu 2
p marc.
p marc. sempre
III.
Spitze
pp
RETURN PRINCIPAL THEME

155
280
riten.
a tempo
Fl.
Ob.
Kl.
Fg.
Hr. (F)
Tr. (F)
Pos.
(B) Tb. (F)
Ktb.
Vl.
Br.
Vo.
Kb.
p marc.
cresc. sempre
ff marc.
dim.
poco a poco cresc.
marc. sempre
cresc.

156
Fl.
Ob.
Kl.
Fg.
Hr. (F)
Tr. (F)
Vl.
Br.
Vo.
zu 2
cresc.
dim.
I.

a tempo
I. ritard. 290
Ob.
zu 2
Hr. (F)
Tr. (F)
Pos.
(B) Tb. (F).
Ktb.
Spitze
pp marc. sempre
Vl.
Br.
Vc. Kb.
pp marc. sempre

Fl.
Ob.
Tr. (F)
poco a poco
cresc.
P marc.
Vl.
pp poco a poco
Br.
Vc.
300
p marc.
mf marc.
Kl.
Fg.
Hr. (F)
(B) Tb. (F)
Spitze
P marc. sempre

Fl.
poco a poco cresc.
ff marc. sempre
Ob.
Kl.
Fg.
Hr. (F)
Tr. (F)
Pos.
f marc. sempre
(B) Tb. (F)
p cresc.
Ktb.
Vl.
cresc. sempre
Br.
Vc. Kb.

310
Fl.
Ob.
Kl.
Fg.
Hr. (F)
Tr. (F)
Pos.
(B) Tb. (F)
Ktb.
Vl.
Br.
Vc. Kb.
cresc.

Sehr breit.
161
Tempo I anfangs noch sehr ruhig
zu 2
Fl.
Ob.
Kl.
Fg.
Hr. (F)
p marc.
Tr. (F)
Pos.
(B) Tb. (F)
Ktb.
Pk.
pp
Vl.
cresc.
Br.
Vc. Kb.

162
CODA
320
Fl
p poco a poco cresc.
Ob.
Kl.
ff marc. sempre
Fg.
Hr (F)
marc. sempre
mf poco a poco cresc.
Tr. (F)
(B) Tb. (F)
marc. sempre
Pk.
Vl.
Br.
Vc. Kb.
ff

163
zu 2
Fl.
Ob.
Kl.
Fg.
marc.
Hr. (F)
Tr. (F)
ff
Pos.
ff marc.
(B) Tb. (F)
Ktb.
Pk.
Vl.
Br.
Vc. Kb.

164
330
zu 2
Fl.
Ob.
Kl.
Fg.
Hr. (F)
Tr. (F)
Pos.
(B) Tb. (F)
Ktb.
Pk.
Vl.
Br.
Vc. Kb.

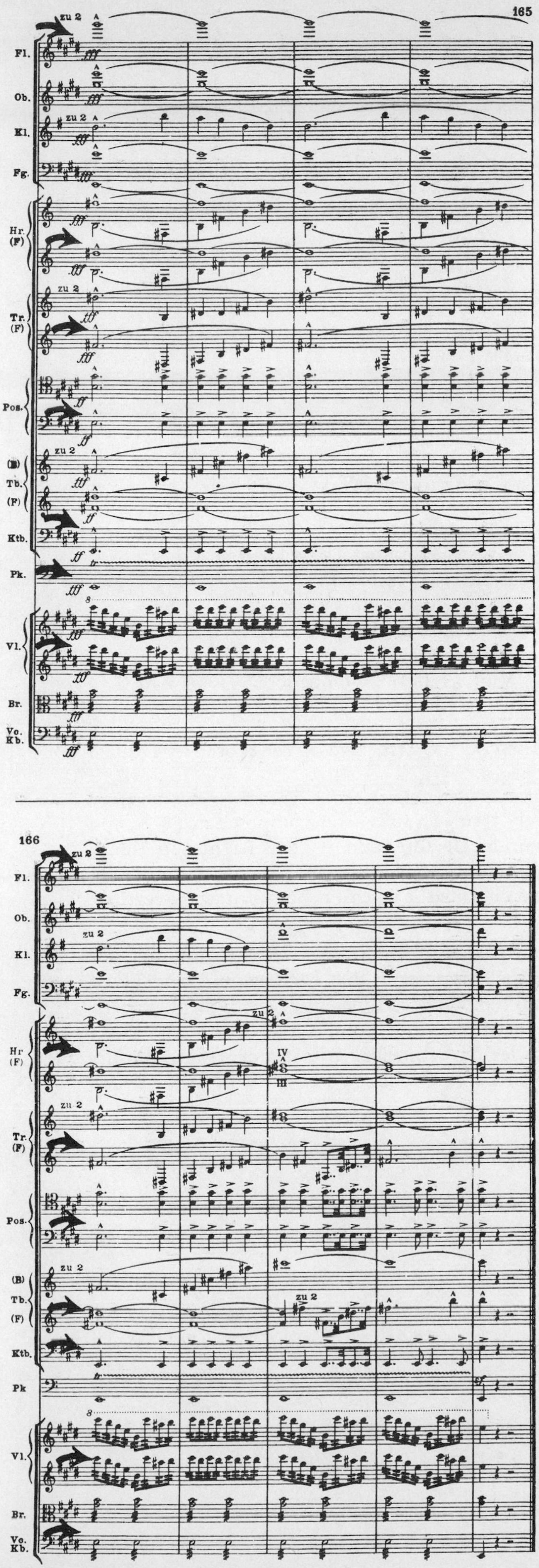
165
zu 2
Fl.
Ob.
Kl.
Fg.
Hr. (F)
Tr. (F)
Pos.
(B) Tb. (F)
Ktb.
Pk.
Vl.
Br.
Vc. Kb.
166
IV
III

"RUSTIC WEDDING" SYMPHONY, Op. 26 — *CARL GOLDMARK*

MOVEMENTS:

I. *Moderato molto (Wedding March)*

II. *Allegretto (Bride's Song)*

III. *Allegro moderato scherzando (Serenade)*

IV. *Andante (In the Garden)*

V. *Allegro molto (The Dance)*

The "Rustic Wedding" Symphony is scored for the following instruments:

2 Flöten (Flutes)	*Fl.*	Triangel (Triangle)	*Tri.*
2 Oboen (Oboes)	*Ob.*	Grosse Trommel (Bass Drum)	*Gr. Tr.*
2 Clarinetten (Clarinets)	*Cl.*	Becken (Cymbals)	*Beck.*
2 Fagotte (Bassoons)	*Fg.*	1. Violinen (1st Violins)	*Viol.*
4 Hörner (Horns)	*Hr.*	2. Violinen (2nd Violins)	*Viol.*
2 Trompeten (Trumpets)	*Tr.*	Bratschen (Violas)	*Br.*
3 Posaunen (Trombones)	*Pos.*	Violoncelle (Violoncellos)	*Vcll.*
2 Pauken (Timpani)	*Pauk.*	Contrabässe (Double Basses)	*Cb.*

Each instrument is listed above under its name as printed on the first page of the score; its English equivalent, and the abbreviation used on succeeding pages.

This symphony, which in form could be more correctly termed a suite, was composed in 1876, and first performed at a Philharmonic concert in Vienna under the direction of Hans Richter in March of that year. It need scarcely be said that the gay Viennese audience received it with tumultuous acclaim in view of the fact that Goldmark had already charmed it with his "Sakuntala" overture.

The five movements of this symphony portray various phases of a country wedding, though not necessarily that of a peasant, for it seems logical that the composer in that event would have given more attention to painting, in a musical sense, the gayly colored costumes and the typical peasant dances. The first movement is a march with thirteen variations; the second is a "Bridal Song" given to the oboe; the third is a serenade; the fourth, entitled "In the Garden", is a charming picture of lovers conversing with each other; the fifth movement is a dance in fugal form, brilliant and picturesque, with a return to the theme of the garden music.

This symphony is recorded by the Vienna Philharmonic Orchestra under the direction of Robert Heger.

Rustic Wedding Symphony

(Ländliche Hochzeit)

I Wedding March

Carl Goldmark, Op. 26

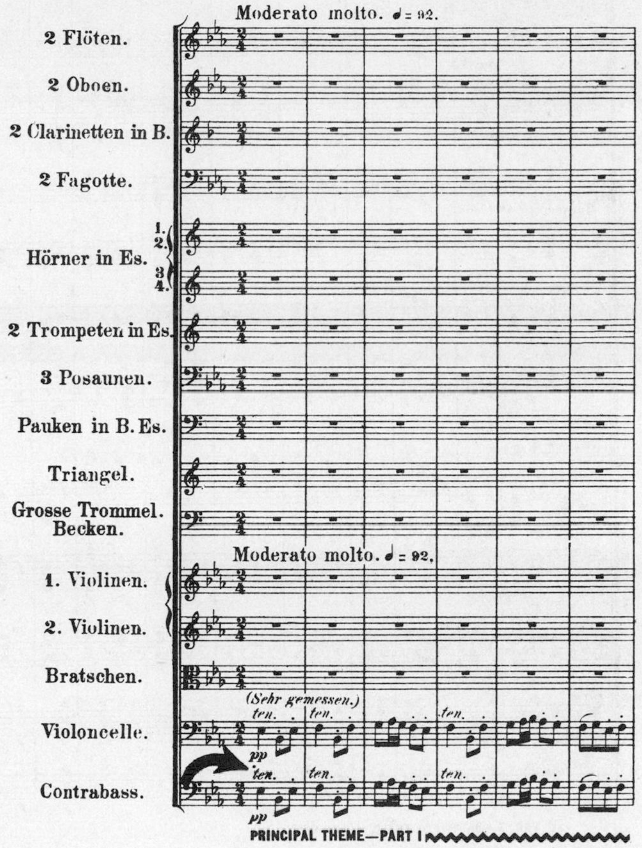

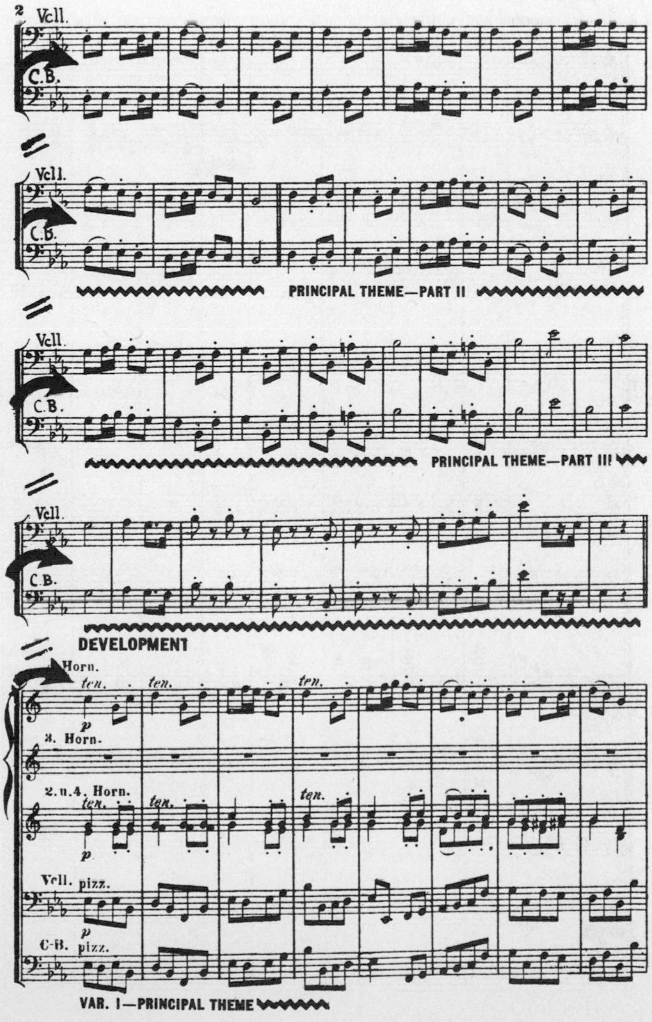

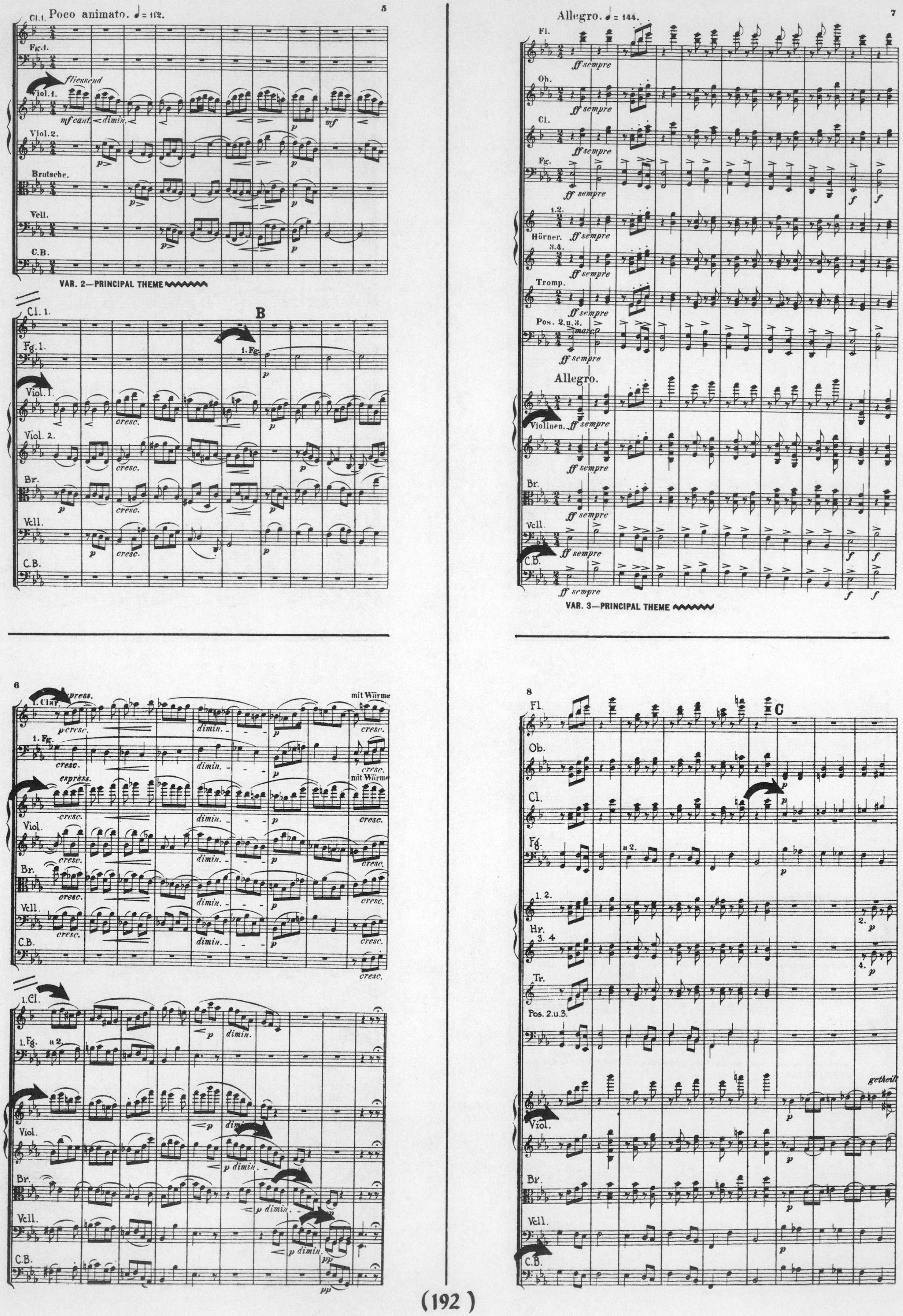
Poco animato. 𝅗𝅥 = 112.
5
Cl. 1.
Fg. 1.
fliessend
Viol. 1.
mf cant. dimin.
Viol. 2.
Bratsche.
Vell.
C.B.
VAR. 2—PRINCIPAL THEME
B
1. Fg.
cresc.
Viol. 2.
Br.
6
espress.
1. Clar.
mit Wärme
dimin.
Viol.
1. Cl.
1. Fg. a 2.
pp
Allegro. 𝅗𝅥 = 144.
7
Fl.
ff sempre
Ob.
Cl.
Fg.
Hörner.
Tromp.
Pos. 2. u. 3.
marc.
Allegro.
Violinen.
VAR. 3—PRINCIPAL THEME
8
C
Hr.
Tr.
Pos. 2. u. 3.
getheilt
Viol.

9
Fl.
a 2.
p cresc.
Ob.
cresc.
Cl.
Fg.
1. 2.
Hr.
3. 4.
Tr.
p cresc.
Pos. 2.u.3.
Viol.
Br.
Vcll.
C.B.

10
Fl.
a 2.
cresc. sempre
Ob.
Cl.
Fg.
1. 2.
Hr.
3. 4.
Tr.
Pos. 2.u.3.
Viol.
Br.
Vcll
C.B.

11
con fuoco
rit. molto
Fl.
Ob.
Cl.
Fg.
a 2.
1. 2.
Hr.
3. 4.
Tr.
Pos. 2.u.3.
Viol.
Br.
Vcll.
C.B.

12
Andante con moto quasi Allegretto. ♪= 144.
Fl.
Ob.
Cl.
Fg.
1. 2.
Hr.
3. 4.
Tr.
Pos. 2.u.3.
espress.
Viol.
Br.
Vcll.
C.B.
dim.
VAR. 4—PRINCIPAL THEME

13

Cl.
Fg.
Hörner. 3 u.4.
Violinen.
Br.
Vcll.
C.B.
rit.
pp
p
Ob.
tempo
D
cresc.
3.Horn.
Viol.
divisi.
Br.
Vcll.
C.B.

15

Fl.
Ob.
p dim.
f
Cl.
Fg.
Hr.
Tr.
Pos.
Viol.
Br.
Vcll.
C.B.

14

Poco meno.
ruhiger
Fl.
Ob.
Cl.
Fg.
Hr.
Tr.
Pos.
Viol.
Br.
Vcll.
C.B.
p

16

E
Fl.
Ob.
Cl.
Fg.
Hr.
Tr.
Tromp.
Pos.
Viol. 1.
Violinen 2.
Br.
Vcll.
C.B.
pp
p

17
stringendo poco
Fl.
Ob.
Cl.
Fg.
Hr.
Tr.
Pos.
2. u. 3. Pos.
stringendo poco
Viol. 1.
Viol. 2.
Br.
Vcll.
C.B.
dim.
18
cresc.
cresc. molto
19
mit Wärme.
20
rit.
dim.
pp

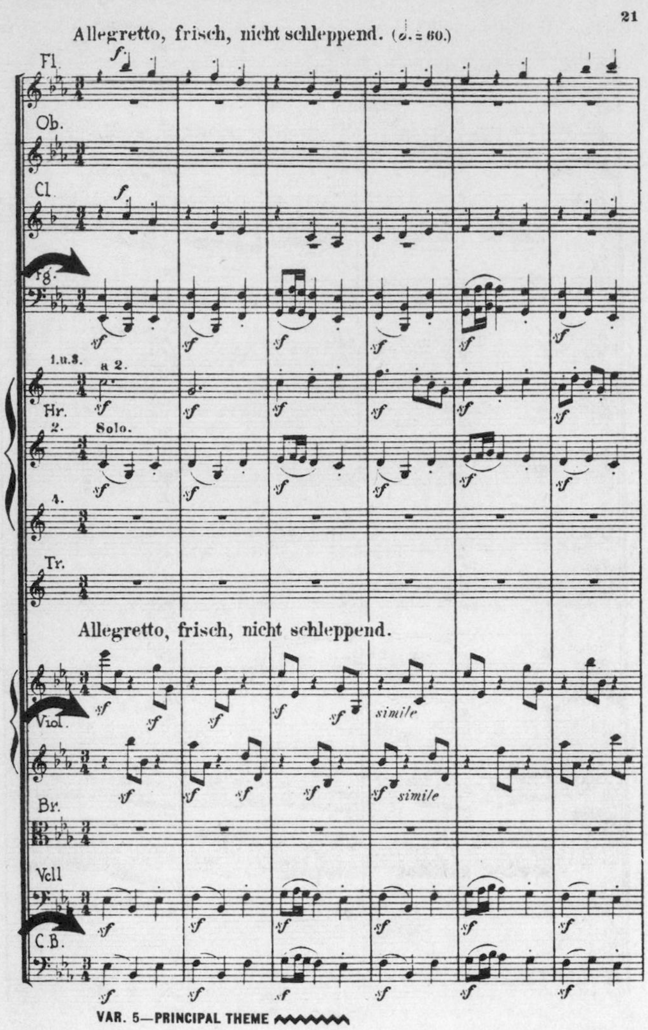
21
Allegretto, frisch, nicht schleppend.
Fl.
Ob.
Cl.
Fg.
1.u.3.
a 2.
Hr.
2.
Solo.
4.
Tr.
Allegretto, frisch, nicht schleppend.
simile
Viol.
simile
Br.
Vcll
C.B.
VAR. 5—PRINCIPAL THEME

22
Fl.
Ob.
Cl.
Fg.
1.u.3.
Hr.
2.
4. Solo.
Tr.
a 2.
Tromp.
Viol.
Br.
Vcll.
C.B

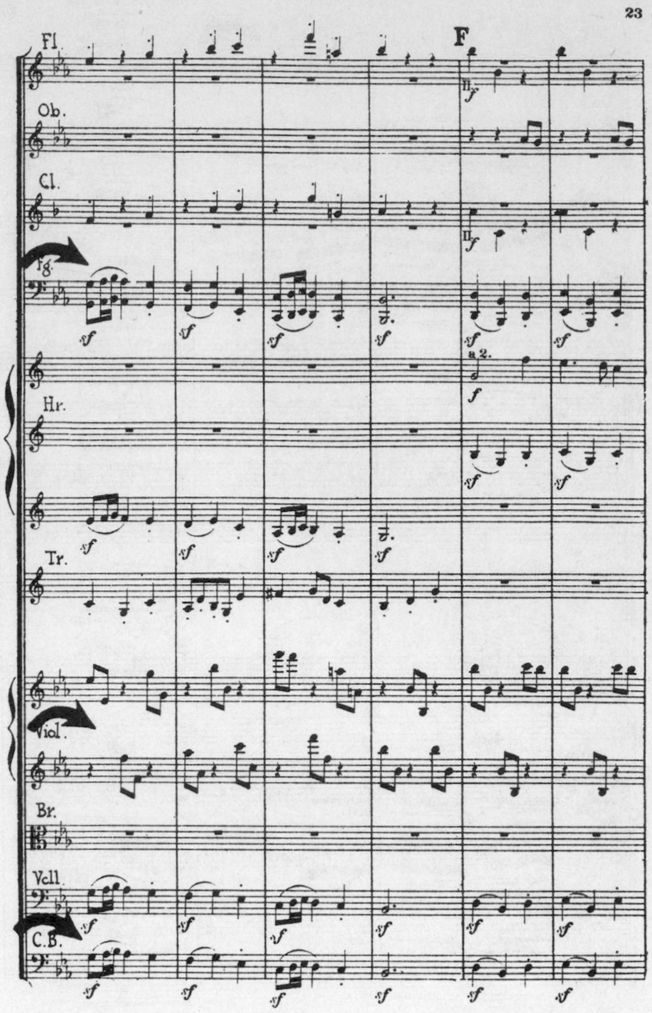
23
Fl.
F
Ob.
Cl.
Fg.
a 2.
Hr.
Tr.
Viol.
Br.
Vcll.
C.B.

24
Fl.
I.
Ob.
Cl.
I.
Fg.
Hr.
3.
Tr.
a 2.
Viol.
Br.
Vcll.
C.B.

25
Fl.
Ob.
Cl.
Fg.
Hr.
Tr.
Viol.
Br.
Vcll.
C.B.
26
staccato sempre
27
Allegro vivace. (leicht und flüchtig.)
p staccato sempre
pp sempre
3.u.4. Horn.
Pos.
p sempre
VAR. 6—PRINCIPAL THEME
28
1.u.2. Horn.
pizz.

29

Fl
G
Ob.
Cl.
Fg.
1.2.
Hr.
3.u.4.Horn
pp
Tr.
Pos.
Viol.
Br.
Vcll.
C.B.

31

Fl
Ob.
Cl.
Fg.
Hr.
Tr.
Pos.
Viol.
Br.
Vcll.
C.B.

30

Fl
cresc.
Ob.
Cl.
Fg.
1.2.
Hr.
3.4.
Tr.
Pos.
Viol.
cresc.
Br.
Vcll.
C.B.

32

Fl
cresc.
Ob.
Cl.
Fg.
1.2.
Hr.
3.u.4.
1.Tromp.
Tr.
Pos.
Viol.
Br.
arco
Vcll.
C.B.

33

Allegretto pesante. 𝅗𝅥 = 152.
(nicht schleppend)
Fl.
a 2.
Ob.
Cl.
Fg.
a 2.
Hr.
Tr.
Pos.
Pauken.
Allegretto pesante. 𝅗𝅥 = 152.
(nicht schleppend)
Viol.
Br.
Vcll.
C.B.
VAR. 7—PRINCIPAL THEME

34

Fl.
Solo.
H
Ob.
espress.
cresc.
Cl.
Fg.
a 2.
Hr.
Tr.
Pos.
Pauk.
Viol.
Br.
Vcll.
C.B.

35

Fl.
Ob.
Cl.
Fg.
Hr.
Tr.
Pos.
Pauk.
Viol.
Br.
Vcl.
C.B.

36

Fl.
I.
dim.
cresc.
ten.
Ob.
Cl.
Fg.
Hr.
Tr.
Pos.
Pauk.
Viol.
Br.
Vcll.
C.B.

VAR. 8—PRINCIPAL THEME

41

42

VAR. 9—PRINCIPAL THEME

43

44

45

47

46

48

VAR. 10—PRINCIPAL THEME

49
Cl.
Fg.
1. 2.
Hörner.
3. 4.
Viol.
Br.
Vell. u. C.B.
cresc.
O
Hr.
3. u. 4.
Ve. u. C.B.

50
Cl.
Fg.
1. 2.
Hr.
3. u. 4.
Viol.
Br.
Vc. u. C.B.
cresc.
Ob.
II.

51
P
Fl.
Ob.
Cl.
Fg.
Hörner.
Tromp.
3. Pos.
Viol.
Br.
Vell
C.B.
f sempre

52
Fl.
Ob.
Cl.
Fg.
Hr.
Tr.
3. Pos.
Viol
Br.
Vell.
C.B.
arco
Arco
pp

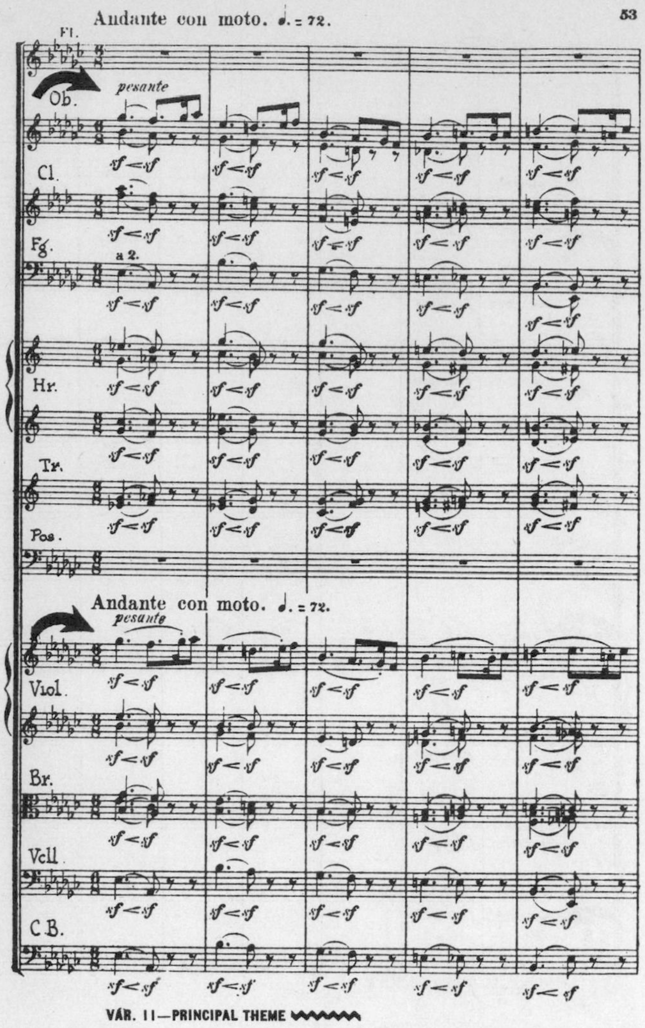
Andante con moto. ♩. = 72.
53
Fl.
Ob.
pesante
Cl.
Fg.
a 2.
Hr.
Tr.
Pos.
Andante con moto. ♩. = 72.
pesante
Viol
Br.
Vcll
C.B.
VAR. II—PRINCIPAL THEME

55
Fl.
Q
cresc.
Ob.
Cl.
I.Solo.
p part
Fg.
Hr.
Tr.
Pos.
p cresc.
Viol
mf
Br.
Vcll.
C.B.

54
Fl.
Ob.
Cl.
Fg.
a 2.
Hr.
Tr.
Pos.
Viol
Br.
Vcll.
C.B.

56
Fl.
ff
dim.
Ob.
Cl.
p dim.
Fg.
Hr.
Tr.
Pos.
Viol
Br.
Vcll.
C.B.

VAR. 12—PRINCIPAL THEME

61

T
Fl. tempo
Ob. tempo
Cl. tempo
Fg. a 2. tempo
Hörner 3.4. tempo
mf
Eine 1te Violine Solo.
Eine 2te Violine Solo.
Eine Bratsche Solo.
p zart
cresc.

62

Fl.
Ob.
a 2.
Cl.
Fg.
Hr.
2. Horn.
3. Horn.
Tr.
Pos.
Viol.
Br.
Vcll.
C.B.

63

U a 2.
Fl.
Fg.
Hr.
Tr.
Pos.
Solo.
Viol. 1. Tutti.
Solo.
Viol. 2. Tutti. geteilt
Solo.
Bratschen. Tutti.
Vcll.
C.B.
ff

64

Fl.
Ob.
Cl.
breit
Fg.
Hr.
Tr.
Pos.
G Saite
breit
Viol.
Br.
Vcll.
C.B.
rit. tempo
f sempre dim. p dim. pp

65
Tempo des Thema. 𝅗𝅥 = 104.
(Etwas belebter.)
Fl.
Ob.
Cl.
Fg.
Hörner.
Tromp.
3 Pos.
Pauken.
Triangel.
Gr. Trommel mit Becken.
Tempo des Thema.
Viol.
Br.
Vcll.
C.B.
ff staccato
VAR. 13—PRINCIPAL THEME

66
Fl.
Ob.
Cl.
Fg.
Hr.
Solo.3
Tr.
3. Pos
Pauk.
Tri
Gr. Tr. u. Beck.
gr. Tr. allein
Viol.
Br.
Vcll.
C.B.
pizz.
p dim. sempre

67
Fl.
Ob.
Cl.
Fg.
Hörner.
Tr.
Pos.
Pauk.
Tri.
Gr. Tr. u. Beck.
Viol.
Br.
Vcll.
C.B.

CODA
68
Fl. V Etwas ruhiger.
Ob.
Cl.
pp sempre
Hörner.
Tr.
Pos.
Pauk.
Triangel.
Gr. Tr. u. Beck.
pizz.
Viol.
Br.
Vcll.
arco
C.B.

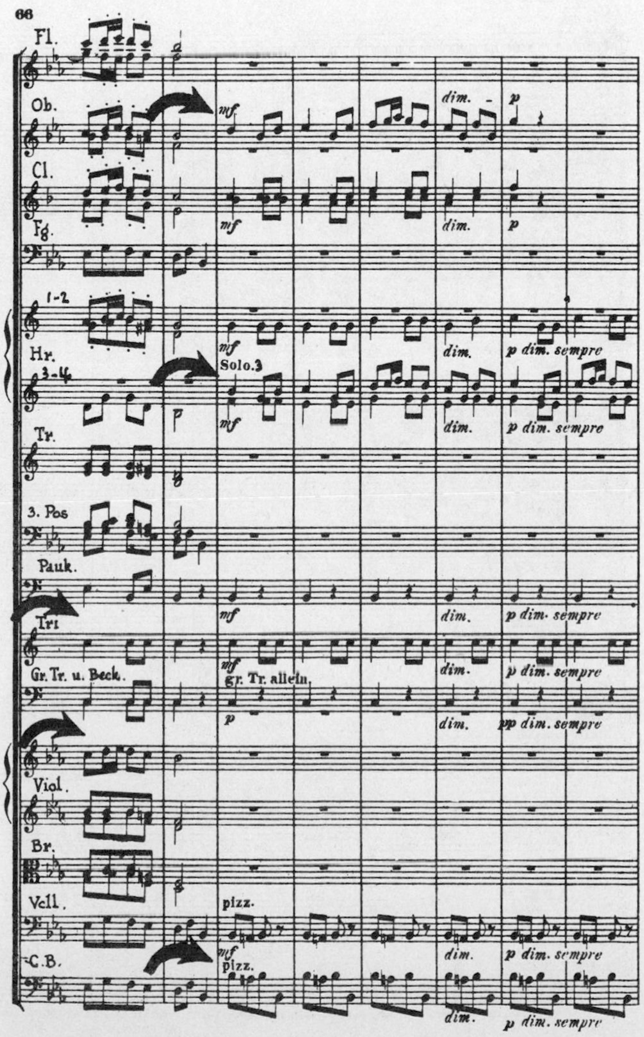

PRINCIPAL THEME—PART I, 2nd PERIOD

Brautlied.

PRINCIPAL THEME—PART I, 1st PERIOD

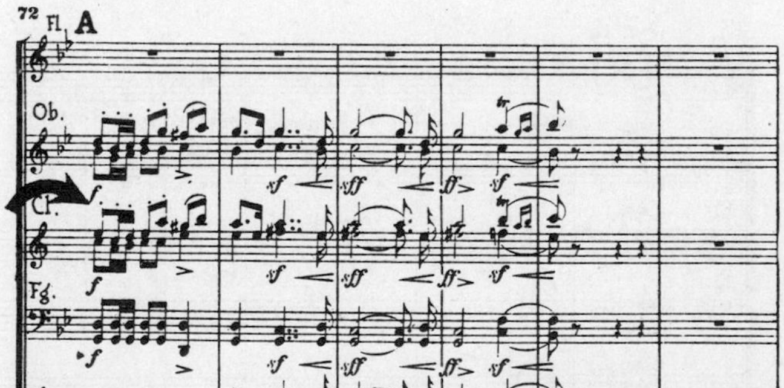

PRINCIPAL THEME—PART II

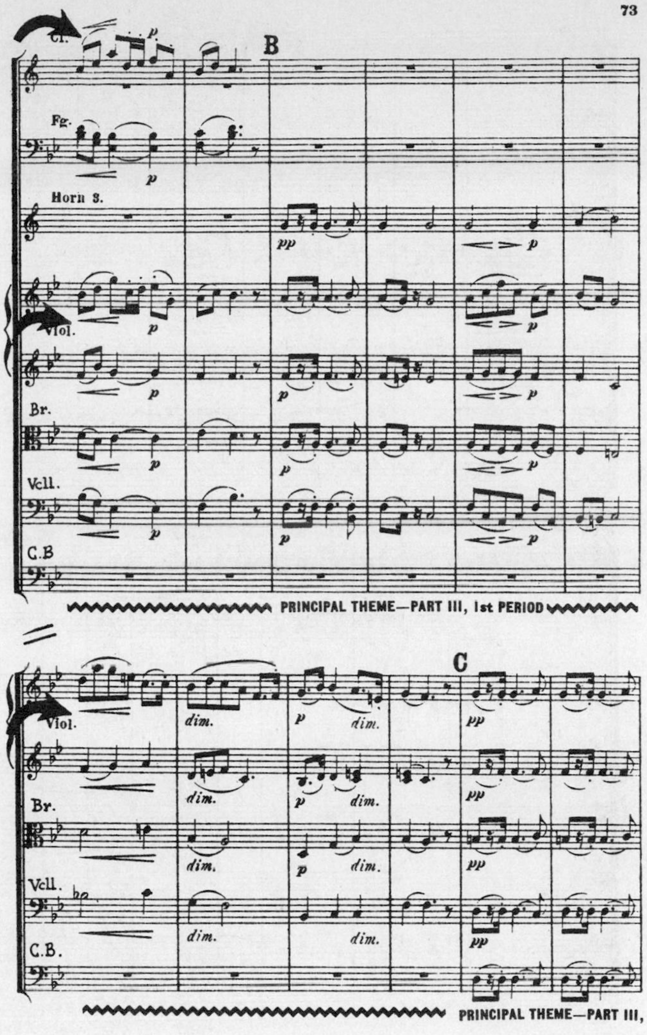
73
Cl.
B
Fg.
Horn 3.
Viol.
Br.
Vcll.
C.B
PRINCIPAL THEME—PART III, 1st PERIOD
C
Viol.
dim.
Br.
Vcll.
C.B.
PRINCIPAL THEME—PART III,

74
Ob.
Fg.
Horn 1.
cresc.
Viol.
Br.
Vcll.
C.B.
2nd PERIOD
D
Ob.
Cl.
Fg. II.
Horn 1.
Viol.
Br.
Vcll.
C.B.
dim.

75
Fl.
E
Ob.
rit.
tempo
Cl.
zart
Fg.
Hr.
Tr.
Pos.
Triangel.
Viol.
pizz.
Br.
arco
Vcll
C.B
RETURN PRINCIPAL THEME—PART I, 1st PERIOD

76
Fl
Ob.
Cl.
Fg.
Hr.
Tr.
Pos.
Tri.
Viol.
arco
Br.
Vcll
C.B.
RETURN PRINCIPAL THEME—PART I, 2nd PERIOD

77
F
Fl.
Ob.
Cl.
Fg.
Hr.
Tr.
Pos.
Tri.
Viol.
Br.
Vcll.
C.B.

79
Ob
Fg.
Hörner 1.2.
Viol.
Br.
Vell.
C.B.
dim.
H
Hr. 1. u. 2.

78
Ob.
Cl.
Fg.
Hörner.
Viol.
Br.
Vcll.
zart
SUBORDINATE THEME—PART I
G
dim.
SUBORDINATE THEME—PART II

80
CODA
Fl.
a 2.
Ob.
Cl.
Fg.
Hr.
Tr.
Pos.
Triangel.
Br.
Vell
C.B.
pizz.
arco
rit.
tempo
RETURN PRINCIPAL THEME—PART I, 1st PERIOD

81
Fl. I
Ob.
Cl.
Fg.
Hr.
Tr.
Pos.
Tr.
Viol.
Br.
Vcll.
C.B.
ten.
pizz.
arco
pp
p

82
Serenade.
Allegro moderato scherzando. 𝅗𝅥 = 92.
(alla breve.)
2 Flöten.
2 Oboen.
2 Clarinetten in A.
2 Fagotte.
Hörner in F.
2 Trompeten in F.
1. Violinen.
2. Violinen.
Bratschen.
Violoncelle.
Contrabass.
PRINCIPAL THEME—PART I

83
Fl.
Ob.
Cl.
Fg.
1. 2. Horn.
Bratsche.
A
Hr. 1 u. 2.
Viol.
Br.
Vcll.
pizz.
arco
PRINCIPAL THEME—PART II

84
Fl.
Cl.
Viol.
Br.
Ob
Fg.
Hr.
Tr.
Vcll.
C.B.
pizz.
arco
ff

Fl.
a 2.
B
Ob.
sart
Cl.
Fg.
a 2.
Hr.
Tr.
Viol.
Br.
Vell.
C.B.
SUBORDINATE THEME—PART I

86

Ob.
Fg.
Viol.
Vell.
I.
II.
Ob.
dim.
Cl.
Fg.
Hörner.
4tes Solo
Tromp.
Viol.
Br.
Vell.
C.B.
SUBORDINATE THEME—PART II

Fl.
a 2.
Ob.
Cl.
I.
Fg.
Hr.
Tr.
Viol
Br.
Vell
C.B.

88

Ob.
Cl.
Fg.
dim.
Hr.
Tr.
Viol.
Br.
Vell.
C.B.

89
C
Fl.
Ob.
mf
Cl
Fg.
p
Hr.
3.Solo.
Tr.
Viol
spiccato
spiccato
Br.
pizz.
mf
Vcll.
pizz.
C.B.
pizz.
90
Ob.
p
Cl.
I
1. 2.
Hörner
3. 4.
Viol.
dimin.
dimin.
Br.
arco
Vcll.
arco
Ob.
Cl.
f
Hr.
Viol.
Br.
Vcll.
91
D
Ob.
rit.
dimin.
a tempo
Cl.
a tempo
Fg.
Hor.
Viol.
Br.
Vcll.
REPETITION SUBORDINATE THEME— PART I
Ob.
Cl.
dimin.
Fg.
Hor.
Br.
pizz.
arco
Vcll.
REP-
92
E
Ob.
Hor.
mf
Viol.
pizz.
pp
Br.
Vcll.
C.B.
ETITION SUBORDINATE THEME—PART II
Ob.
stacc.
Fg.
Viol.
arco
pp sempre
Br.
Vcll.
C.B.

93

95

BRIDGE PASSAGE ～～～ RETURN PRINCIPAL THEME—PART I ～～～

94

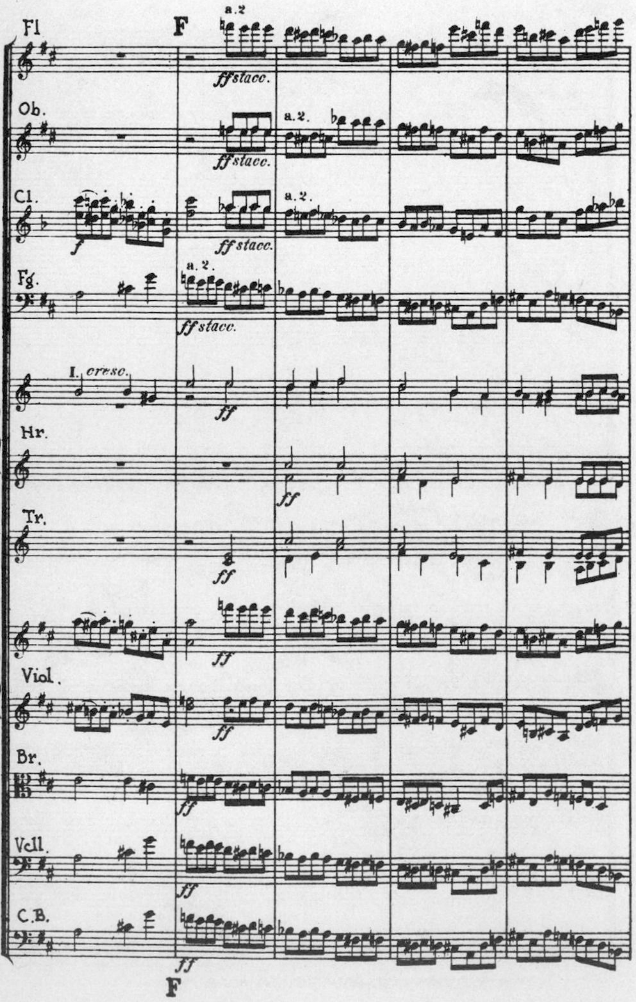

96

～～～ RETURN PRINCIPAL THEME—PART II ～～～

97
Fl. 1.
Ob.
Cl.
Viol.
Br.
Vell.
arco
pizz.
I.
p
cresc.
J
a 2
Fg.
f
98
f sempre
Hr.
Tr.
C.B.
99
K
ff
100
sf
dim.
dimin.
BRIDGE PASSAGE
p
pp

101
Cl.
rit.
a tempo
gener.
Viol.
Br.
Vell.
C.B.
pizz.
RETURN SUBORDINATE THEME—PART I

Cl.
Fg.
Viol.
Br.
Vell.
C.B.
arco
pizz.

102
Ob
L
Cl.
Fg.
Hörner 3.4.
Viol.
stacc.
dimin.
Br.
Vell.
C.B.
Ob.
Fg.
Hörner 3.4.
Viol.
Br.
Vell.

103
Ob
Fag.
cresc.
Hörner 3.4
stacc.
Viol.
Br.
Vell.
CODA
M
Cl.
Fag.
1. 2.
Hörner
3. 4.
pizz.
Viol.
Br.
Vell. pizz.

104
Fl.
Ob.
Cl.
dimin.
Fag.
Hr.
Tr.
Viol.
Br.
Vell.
C.B.

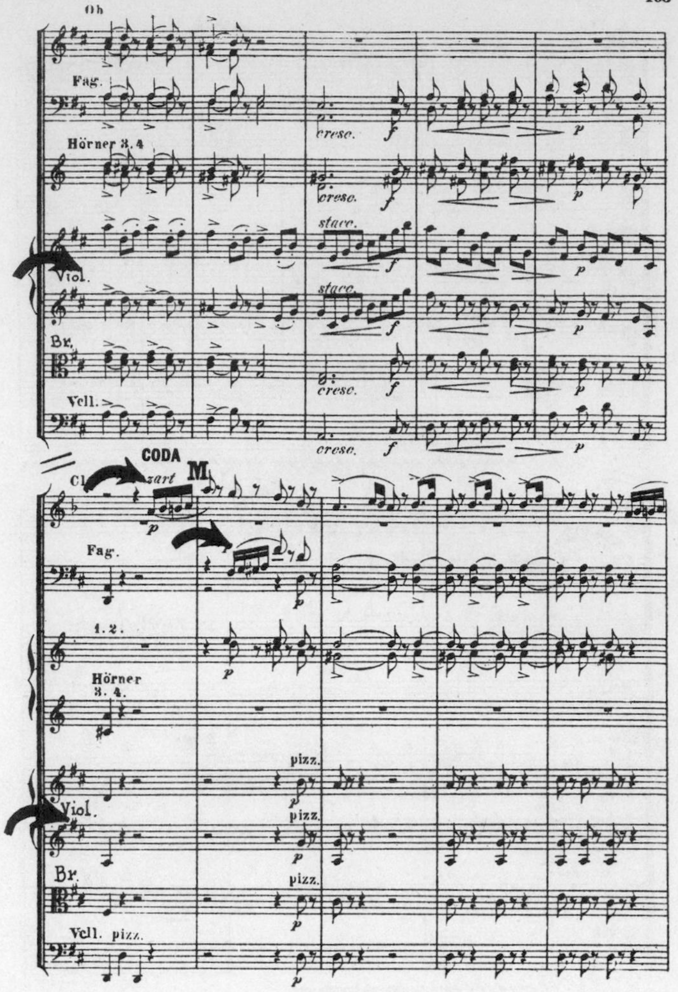

105
N
Fl.
Ob.
Cl.
Fg.
pp
Hr.
Tr.
arco
Viol.
Br.
Vcll.
C.B.
N

107
Fl.
Ob.
Cl.
Fg.
Hr.
Tr.
(geth.)
pizz.
Viol.
Br.
Vcll.
C.B.

106
Fl.
p stacc.
Ob
Cl.
Fg.
Hr.
Tr.
Viol.
Br.
Vcll.
pizz.
C.B.

108
Im Garten.
EXPOSITION
Andante. ♩ = 72.
2 Flöten.
2 Oboen.
2 Clarinetten in B.
Sehr zart und träumerisch.
2 Fagotte.
1.2.
Hörner in F.
3.4.
2 Trompeten in F.
3 Posaunen.
Andante. ♩ = 72.
1.Violinen.
2.Violinen.
Bratschen.
Violoncelle.
(geth.)
p > dimin. pp
Contrabass.
PRINCIPAL THEME

109
Ob.
Cl.
Br.
Vell.
C.B.
A
sehr zart.
Hor. I. II.
Viol.
REPETITION PRINCIPAL THEME

110
Fl.
Ob.
Cl.
Fg.
Hr.
Tr.
Pos.
Viol.
Br.
Vell.
C.B.
f espress. molto

111
Fl.
Ob.
Cl.
Fg.
Hr.
Tr.
Pos
Viol.
Br.
Vell.
C.B.
BRIDGE PASSAGE

112
Poco più lento.
Viol.
Br.
Vell.
SUBORDINATE THEME—PART I
Ob.
Fag.
Hörner. 1.2.
B
Solo.
SUBORDINATE

113
Ob.
cresc. molto
espress
Cl.
dim.
p zart.
Fag.
pp
Viol.
pp
Br.
Vell.
THEME—PART II
string.
f sempre
Hor. 3.
3 Solo.
mit Leidenschaft
string. poco
espress. molto
cresc. molto sempre molto

114
C
in tempo
Fl.
Ob.
espress. molto
dim. p
Cl.
Fg.
3. Hor.
Tr.
Pos.
Viol.
Br.
Vcll.
C.B.

DEVELOPMENT 115
D wieder ruhig
rit.
Fl.
Ob.
dim. pp
zart.
Cl.
Fg.
Hor. 1.
canto
Hr.
Tr.
Pos.
Viol.
pp sempre
Br.
p ruhig
Vcll.
pizz.
C.B.
DEVELOPMENT—SECTION I

116
Fl.
Ob.
p zart.
Cl.
Fg.
Hr
espress.
Tr.
Pos.
Viol.
Br.
Vcll.
C.B.

E
117
Fl.
Ob.
Cl.
Fg.
Hr.
Tr.
Pos.
1. Pos.
1. Viol.
2. Viol.
Br.
Vcll.
arco
C.B.
arco
cresc.
f cresc. molto
mf cresc.
p cresc.

118
Fl.
a 2. mit Wärme
espress.
Ob.
mit Wärme
Cl.
Fg.
a 2.
Hr.
Tr.
Pos.
1. Viol
2. Viol.
Br.
Vcll
C.B.
ff mit Wärme

119
Fl.
Ob.
espress.
Cl.
Fg.
Hr.
Tr.
Pos
1. Viol.
2. Viol.
Br.
Vcll
C.B.
dim. pp

120
F
Ob.
1 Solo
p zart.
Cl.
Fag.
zart.
Viol.
Br.
Vcll.
espress.
cresc. molto
espress. molto
ten.
dim

121
Fl.
I.
Ob.
heftig
f string. poco
Cl.
f string. poco
Fg.
heftig
Hr.
Tr.
f string. poco
Viol.
f string. poco
Br.
Vcll.
heftig
f string. poco
C.B.

123
Fl.
a 2.
Ob.
Cl.
Fg.
1.3.
Hörner.
2.4.
Tr.
Pos.
Viol.
Br.
Vcll.
C.B.

122
in tempo
Fl.
G
ff mit Wärme
acceler. poco
Ob.
mit Wärme
dim.
pp
ff acceler. poco
Cl.
mit Wärme
ff acceler. poco
Fg.
a 2.
acceler. poco
espress.
Hr.
ff sempre
Tr.
ff sempre
Posaunen.
2.3.
in tempo
ff mit Wärme
Viol.
acceler. poco
ff sempre
Br.
ff sempre
Vcll.
C.B.
acceler. poco

124
Fl.
a 2.
Ob.
Cl.
Fg.
a 2.
1.2.
Hörner.
3.4.
Tr.
Pos.
Viol.
Br.
Vcll.
C.B.

125

RETURNING PASSAGE (RETRANSITION)

126

RECAPITULATION

127

128

REPETITION PRINCIPAL THEME

129
Fl.
Ob.
espress. molto
Cl.
espress.
Fg.
Hr.
Tr.
Pos.
Viol.
espress.
espress. molto
Br.
Vcll.
f espress. molto
C.B.

130
CODA
Etwas zurückhaltend.
äusserst zart.
Fl.
Ob.
Cl.
Fg.
Hr.
Tr.
Pos.
Etwas zurückhaltend.
äusserst zart.
Viol.
Br.
Vcll.
C.B.
pizz.
arco

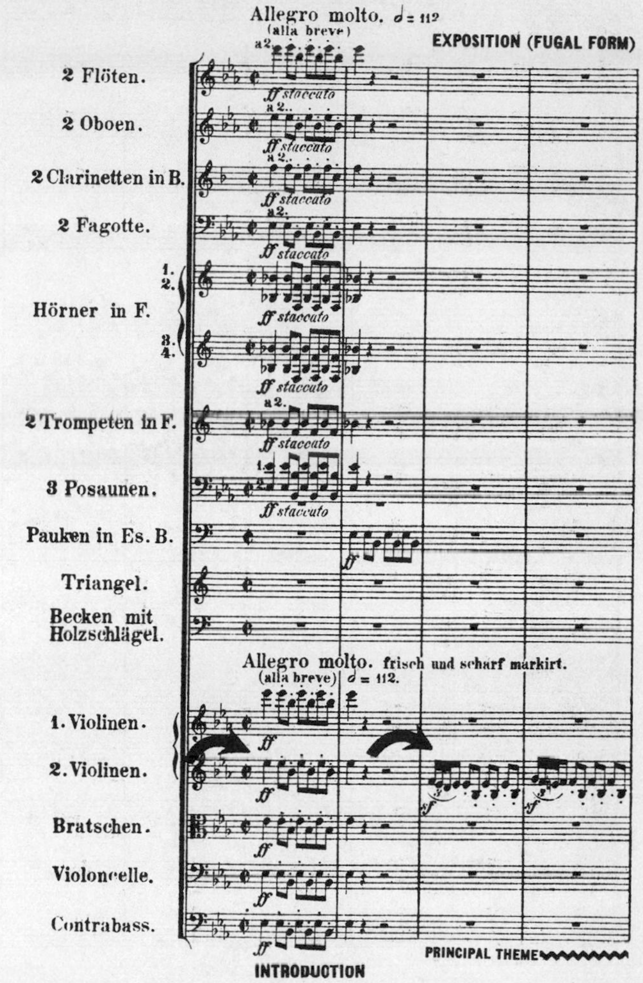
Tanz.
131
Allegro molto. 𝅗𝅥 = 112
(alla breve)
EXPOSITION (FUGAL FORM)
2 Flöten.
2 Oboen.
2 Clarinetten in B.
2 Fagotte.
Hörner in F.
2 Trompeten in F.
3 Posaunen.
Pauken in Es. B.
Triangel.
Becken mit Holzschlägel.
ff staccato
Allegro molto. frisch und scharf markirt.
(alla breve) 𝅗𝅥 = 112.
1. Violinen.
2. Violinen.
Bratschen.
Violoncelle.
Contrabass.
INTRODUCTION
PRINCIPAL THEME

132
Viol.
f sempre
Br.
Vcll.
C.B.

133
Viol.
f sempre
Br.
Vcll.
C.B.
A
Fl.
Ob.
Cl.
Fg.
Tromp.
pp

135
Fl
Ob.
Cl.
Fg.
Hr.
Tr.
Pos.
Pauk.
Tri.
Beck.
Viol.
Br
Vcll.
C.B.

134
Fl.
Ob.
Cl.
Fg.
Hr.
Tromp.
Pos
Pauk.
Tri.
Beck.
Viol
Br.
Vcll.
C.B.

136
B
Fl
Ob.
Cl.
Fg.
Hr.
Tr.
Pos.
Pauk.
Tri.
Beck.
Viol.
Br.
Vcll.
C.B.

137
Fl.
Ob.
Cl.
Fg.
a 2.
Hr.
Tr.
Pos.
Pauk.
Tri.
Beck.
Viol.
Br.
Vcll.
C.B.

138
Fl.
a 2.
Ob.
Cl.
Fg.
Hr.
Tr.
Pos.
Pauk.
Tri.
Beck.
Viol.
Br.
Vcll.
C.B.

139
C
Fl.
a 2.
Ob.
Cl.
Fg.
Hr.
Tr.
Pos.
Pauk.
Tri.
Beck.
Viol.
Br.
Vcll.
C.B.
SUBORDINATE THEME

140
Fl.
a 2.
Ob.
Cl.
Fg.
Hr.
Tr.
1.2.
Pos. 3.
Pauken.
Triangel.
Becken mit Holzschägel.
Viol.
Br.
Vcll.
C.B.

141
Fl.
Ob.
Cl.
Fg.
Hr.
Tr.
Pos.
Pauk.
Tri.
Beck.
Viol.
Br.
Vcll.
C.B.

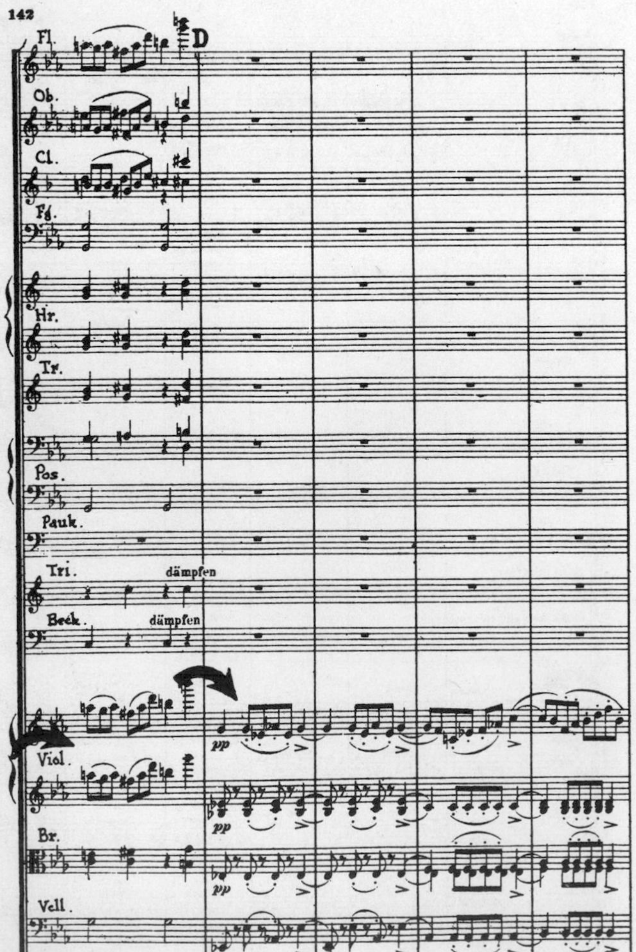
142
Fl.
D
Ob.
Cl.
Fg.
Hr.
Tr.
Pos.
Pauk.
Tri.
dämpfen
Beck.
dämpfen
Viol.
pp
Br.
pp
Vcll.
pp
C.B.

143
Fl.
a 2.
ff
Ob.
Cl.
Fg.
Hr.
pp
Tr.
Pos.
Pauk
Tri.
Beck.
f
Viol.
Br.
Vcll.
C.B
CODETTA

144
DEVELOPMENT
E
Fl
Ob.
Cl.
pp
Fg
Hr.
Tr.
Pos.
Pauk.
Tri.
Beck.
Viol.
grazioso
Br.
pizz.
arco
Vcll.
pizz.
arco
zart
C.B.
pizz.
DEVELOPMENT—SECTION I

145

DEVELOPMENT—SECTION 2

146

147

148

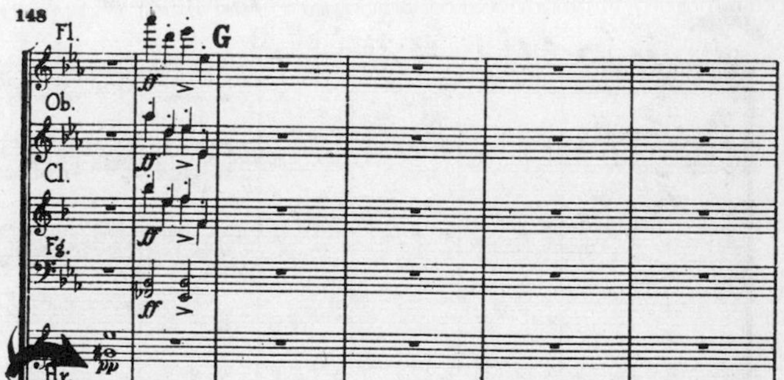

RETURNING PASSAGE (RETRANSITION)

RECAPITULATION

RETURN PRINCIPAL THEME

153
Fl.
a 2.
Ob.
Cl.
Fg.
Hr.
Tr.
Pos.
Pauk.
Tri.
Beck.
Viol.
Br.
Vcll.
C.B.
155
staccato
p cresc.
156
rit. molto
dim.

RETURN PRINCIPAL THEME (FROM FOURTH MOVEMENT)

RETURN SUBORDINATE THEME

161
Fl.
Ob.
Cl.
Fg.
Hr.
Tr.
Pos.
Pauk.
Tri.
(dämpfen)
Beck.
(dämpfen)
Viol.
Br.
Vcll.
C.B.
RETURN CODETTA

K
163
Ob.
tempo
Cl.
tempo
Fg.
tempo
Viol.
tempo
Br.
Vcll.
C.B. pizz.
Fl.
cresc. sempre
a 2.
Ob.
Cl.
Fg.
Viol.
Br.
Vcll.
C.B.

162
CODA
I
Fl.
Ob.
Cl.
Fg.
Hr.
Tr.
Pos.
Vi
Br.
Vcll.
C.B.
CODA—SECTION I
Viol.
Br.
Vcll.
C.B.
cresc.
dim.
rit.

164
Fl.
I. Solo.
Ob.
Cl.
I. Solo.
Fg.
Hr.
Tr.
Pos.
Pauken.
Viol.
Br.
Vcll.
C.B.
arco

165

166

167

168

170

CODA—SECTION 3

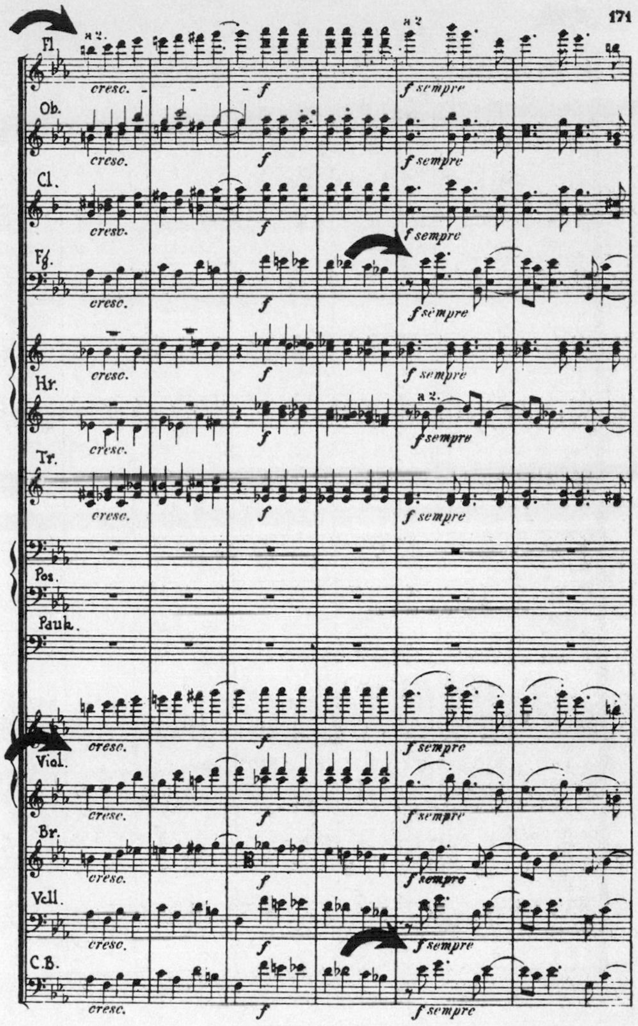

172

CODA—SECTION 4

CODA—SECTION 5

"NEW WORLD" SYMPHONY, Op. 95 — *ANTONIN DVOŘÁK*

MOVEMENTS:

- I. *Adagio-Allegro molto*
- II. *Largo*
- III. *Scherzo—Molto vivace*
- IV. *Allegro con fuoco*

The "New World" Symphony is scored for the following instruments:

2 Flauti (Flutes)	*Fl.*
2 Oboi (Oboes)	*Ob.*
2 Clarinetti (Clarinets)	*Cl.*
1 Cor. inglese (English Horn)	*Cor. ingl.*
2 Fagotti (Bassoons)	*Fag.*
4 Corni (Horns)	*Cor.*
2 Trombe (Trumpets)	*Tr.*
3 Tromboni (Trombones)	*Trb.*
1 Tuba (Tuba)	*Tb.*
3 Timpani (Tympani)	*Tym.*
Triangolo (Triangle)	*Tri.*
Piatti (Cymbals)	*Pia.*
1. Violini (1st Violins)	*Viol.*
2. Violini (2nd Violins)	*Viol.*
Violo (Violas)	*Vla.*
Violoncelli (Violoncellos)	*Vc.*
Contrabassi (Double Basses)	*Cb.*

Each instrument is listed above under its name as printed on the first page of the score; its English equivalent, and the abbreviation used on succeeding pages.

Dvořák made his preliminary sketches for this symphony in 1892-93 while he was director of the National Conservatory of Music in New York. His manuscript books indicate that he began it in 1892 and completed it in 1893. The first performance was given by the Philharmonic Society of New York on December 15, 1893. Anton Seidl was the conductor and Dvořák himself was present.

The symphony was well received, but a controversy arose as to whether some of the themes were original, or taken from American Indian or negro folk songs. In connection with this, when Oskar Nedbal was preparing to conduct the symphony at Berlin in 1900, Dvořák wrote as follows to Nedbal: "I am sending you Kretzschmar's analysis of the symphony, but omit that nonsense about my having made use of 'Indian' and 'American' themes—that is a lie. I tried to write only in the spirit of those national American melodies".

There are three recordings of the "New World" Symphony: one by the Philadelphia Orchestra under Leopold Stokowski, another by the Berlin State Opera Orchestra with Eric Kleiber conducting, and a third by the Hallé Orchestra under the baton of Hamilton Harty.

Symphony Nº 5
(From the New World)

Ant. Dvořák, Op. 95
Adagio. M.M. 𝅘𝅥𝅮 = 126. INTRODUCTION
Flauti.
Oboi.
Clarinetti in A.
Fagotti.
Corni I. II. in E.
Corni III. IV. in C.
Trombe in E.
Tromboni I. II.
Trombone basso.
Tympani A. E. H.
Adagio. M.M. 𝅘𝅥𝅮 = 126.
Violino I.
Violino II.
Viola.
Violoncello.
Contrabasso.

Fl.
Ob.
Cl.
Fag.
Cor.
Tr.
Trb. 1. 2.
Trb. bs.
Tym.
Viol.
Vla.
Vc.
C.B

Fl.
Ob.
Cl.
Fag.
Cor.
Tr.
Trb. 1. 2.
Trb. bs.
Tym.
Viol.
Vla.
Vc.
C.B.

Fl.
Ob.
Cl.
Fag.
Cor.
Tr.
Trb. 1. 2.
Trb. bs.
Tym.
Viol.
Vla.
Vc.
C.B.

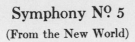

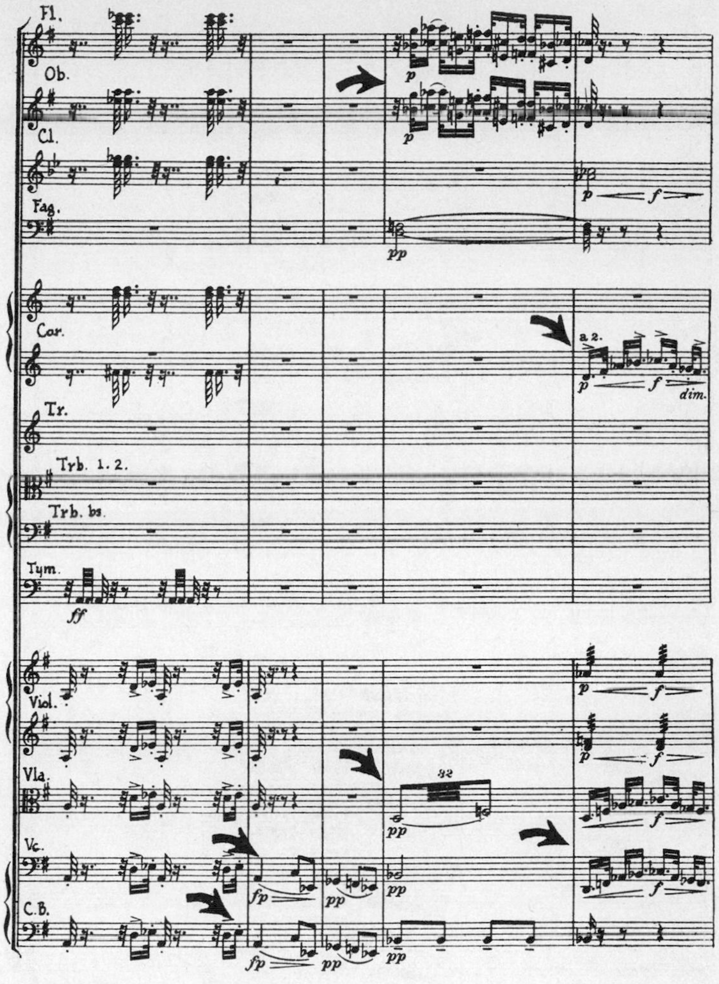

7

8

EXPOSITION

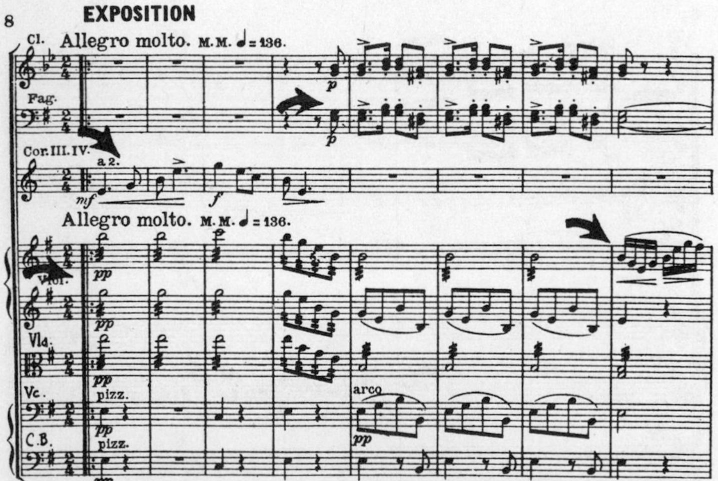

PRINCIPAL THEME—PART I, 1st PERIOD

PRINCIPAL THEME—PART I, 2nd PERIOD

9

PRINCIPAL THEME—PART II

10

11
12
13
14
1
2
Fl.
Ob.
Cl.
Fag.
Cor.
Tr.
Trb. I. II.
Trb. bs.
Tym.
Viol.
Vla.
Vc.
C.B.
a 2.
I.
pizz.
dim.
PRINCIPAL THEME—
PART III

15
Cl.
Fag.
Viol.
Vla.
Vc.
C.B.
sempre più dim.
dim.
17
Fl.
Ob.
cresc.
molto
non legato
arco
SUBORDINATE THEME—PART II
Cl.
16
Cor. III. Solo
pizz.
SUBORDINATE THEME—PART I
Cor. III.
18
Cor. III. IV.
Tymp.
SUBORDINATE

19
Fl.
Ob.
Cl.
Fag.
Viol.
Vla.
Vc.
C.B.
cresc.
dim.
THEME—PART III
20
5 Solo.
CODETTA
21
pizz.
arco
22
Cor.
a 2.
Tr.
in C.
Trb. I. II.
Trb. bs.
Tym.

23
Fl.
Ob.
Cl.
Fag.
Cor.
Tr.
Trb. I. II.
Trb. bs.
Tym.
Viol.
Vla.
Vc.
C.B.
fpp

25
Cl.
Solo.
Cor. III. IV.
Trb.
dim.
Viol.
leggiero
Vla.
Vc.
C.B.
DEVELÖPMENT—SECTION 2
Fl.
Fl. Piccolo.
Cl.
Cor. I.
Solo
Trb.
Trombe Solo.
Viol.
Vla.
Vc.
C.B.
pizz.
ppp

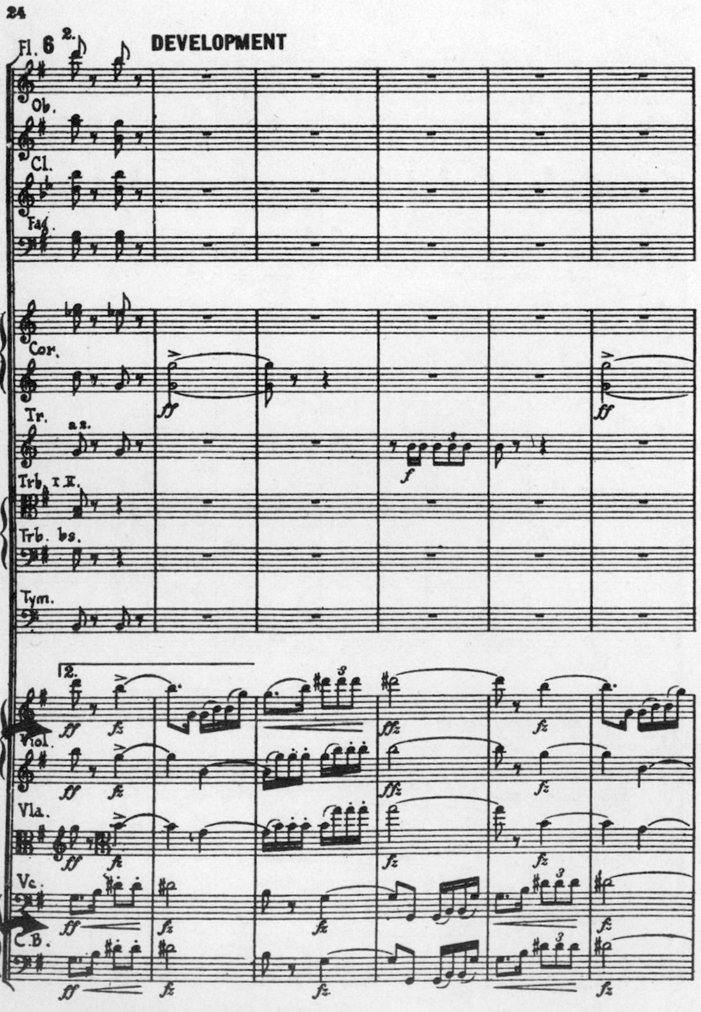
24
DEVELOPMENT
Fl.
Ob.
Cl.
Fag.
Cor.
Tr.
a2.
Trb. I. II.
Trb. bs.
Tym.
Viol.
Vla.
Vc.
C.B.
ff
fz
DEVELOPMENT—SECTION I

26
Fl.
Ob.
Cl.
Fag.
Cor.
poco
Tr.
Trb. I. II.
Trb. b.s.
Tym.
Viol
Vla.
Vc.
pizz.
arco
C.B.
poco

27

Plauto gr. II.
Ob.
Cl.
Fag.
Cor.
Tr.
Trb. I. II.
Trb. bs.
Tym.
Viol.
Vla.
Vc.
C.B.
a poco cresc.
cresc.
più

28

Fl.
Ob.
Cl.
Fag.
a 2.
Cor.
Tr.
Trb. I. II.
Trb. bs.
Tym.
Viol.
sul G.
Vla.
div.
non div.
Vc.
C.B.
arco

29

Fl.
Ob.
a 2.
Cl.
Fag.
Cor.
Tr.
Trb. I. II.
Trb. bs.
Tym.
Viol.
Vla.
div.
Vc.
C.B.

30

Fl.
Ob.
Cl.
Fag.
Cor.
Tr.
a 2.
Trb. I. II.
Trb. bs.
Tym.
Viol.
Vla.
non div.
Vc.
C.B.

31

32

DEVELOPMENT—SECTION 3

33

34

35

37

36

RETURNING PASSAGE (RETRANSITION)

38

RECAPITULATION

RETURN PRINCIPAL THEME—PART I, 1st PERIOD

RETURN PRINCIPAL THEME—PART I, 2nd

39

PERIOD
RETURN PRINCIPAL THEME—PART II

41

PART I

40

42

RETURN SUBORDINATE THEME—PART II

43

Cl.
Fag.
Viol.
Vla.
Vc.
C.B.
pizz.
11
Fl.
Ob.
molto cresc.
cresc.

44

Fl.
Ob.
Cl.
Fag.
Cor.
Trb.
Viol.
Vla.
Vc.
C.B.
arco
dim.
RETURN SUBORDINATE THEME
Viol. I.
II.
PART III

45

Fl.
Ob.
Fag.
Viol.
Vla.
Vc.
C.B.
dim.
cresc.

46

Fl.
Ob.
12
Solo.
Viol.
Vla.
Vc.
C.B.
RETURN CODETTA
Fag.
pizz.

47

Ob.
Cl.
Fag.
p
cresc.
mf
Viol.
Vla.
Vc.
C.B.
arco
CODA
Fl.
Ob.
Cl.
Fag.
Cor.
a 2.
in E
f
CODA—SECTION 1

48

13
Fl.
Ob.
Cl.
Fag.
Cor.
Tr.
in C.
a 2.
Trb. I. II
Trb. bs.
Tym.
Viol.
Vla.
Vc.
C.B.
fff
fz
CODA—SECTION 2

49

Fl.
Ob
Cl
Fag.
Cor.
Tr.
Trb. I. II.
Trb. bs.
Tym.
Viol.
Vla
Vc.
C.B.
ff
fz

50

Fl.
Ob.
Cl.
Fag.
Cor.
ff
Tr.
Trb. I. II.
Trb. bs.
f
Tym.
Viol.
Vla.
div.
Vo.
C.B.
fz

51

53

CODA—SECTION 3

52

54

55

II.

INTRODUCTION

PRINCIPAL

56

THEME—PART I PRINCIPAL THEME—PART II

PRINCIPAL THEME—PART III

57

PRINCIPAL THEME—PART IV

58

PRINCIPAL THEME—PART V

Un poco più mosso.
Fl.
Ob.
Cor. I.II. con sordini
senza sord.
Viol.
Vla.
Vc.
C.B.
CODETTA
SUBORDINATE THEME—
PART I

poco ritard.
Poco meno mosso.
Fl.
Ob.
Cl.
in A.
Fag.
a 2.
Viol.
molto cresc.
div.
Vla.
Vc.
C.B.
pizz.
SUBORDINATE THEME—PART II

Fl.
Ob.
Cl.
Viol.
pizz.
Vla.
Vc.
C.B

3 Poco più mosso.
Fl.
Ob.
Cl.
a 2.
Poco piu mosso.
Viol.
arco
Vla.
Vc.
C.B.
REPETITION SUBORDINATE THEME—PART I

63

Fl.
Ob.
Cl.
Viol.
Vla.
Vc.
C.B.
cresc.
f
ff
mf
dim.
fp
Meno.
sul G
pizz.
pp
ppp
arco
tremolo
REPETITION SUBORDINATE THEME—

65

Ob.
Viol.
Vla.
Vc.
C.B.
dim.
CODETTA
Fl.
Ob.
a 2.
Cl.
p leggiero
cresc.
pp cresc.

64

Cl.
Viol.
Vla.
Vc.
C.B.
cresc.
PART II
mf
dim.
p
pp
arco

66

Fl.
Ob.
Cl.
Fag.
Cor.
Tr.
Trb. I. II.
Trb. bs.
Tym.
Viol.
Vla.
Vc.
C.B.
a 2.
cresc.
mf
p

67

RETURNING PASSAGE (RETRANSITION)

69

RETURN PRINCIPAL THEME—PART I

68

70

RETURN PRINCIPAL THEME—PART II

RETURN PRIN

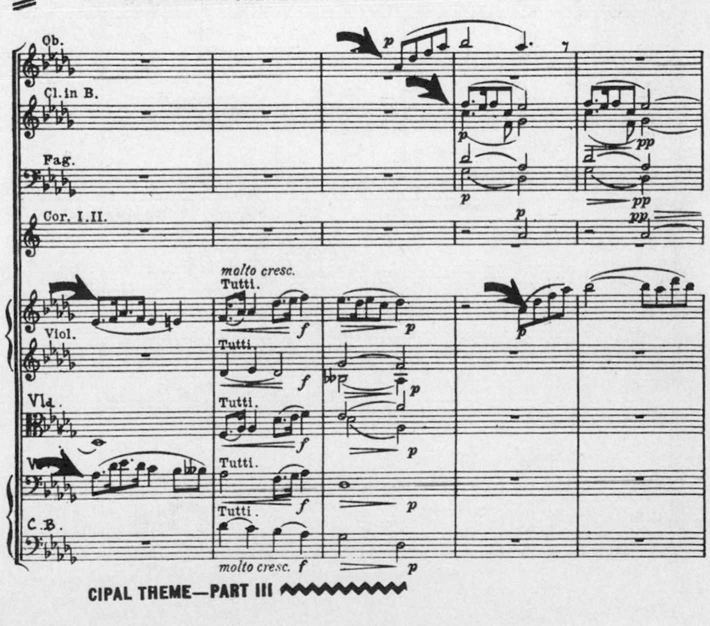

CIPAL THEME—PART III

71
CODA
ritard.
in tempo
Fl.
Ob.
Cl.
Fag.
Cor.
in E. a 2.
Tr.
Trb. I. II.
Trb. bs.
a 2.
Tym.
Viol.
dimin.
dim.
ritard.
in tempo
Vla.
Vc.
C.B.

72
ritard. Molto Adagio.
Fl.
Ob.
Cl.
Fag.
p dim.
Cor.
Tr.
Trb. I. II.
Trb. bs
Tym.
ritard. Molto Adagio.
Viol.
dim.
Vla.
Vc.
C.B
div.

III. Scherzo.
73
Molto Vivace. INTRODUCTION
PRINCIPAL SECTION
Flauti.
Oboi.
Clarinetti in A.
Fagotti.
Corni I. II. in E.
Corni III. IV. in E.
Trombe in E.
Tympani E. & H.
Triangolo.
Molto Vivace. M. M. 𝅗𝅥. = 80.
Violino I.
Violino II.
Viola.
Violoncello.
Contrabasso.

74
Fl.
Ob.
Cl.
Viol.
pizz.
dim.
Vla.
C.B.
PRINCIPAL THEME—PART I
Fl.
Ob.
Cl.
Cor. III.
Tymp.
Solo.
Viol.
arco
pizz.
Vla.
Vc.
C.B.

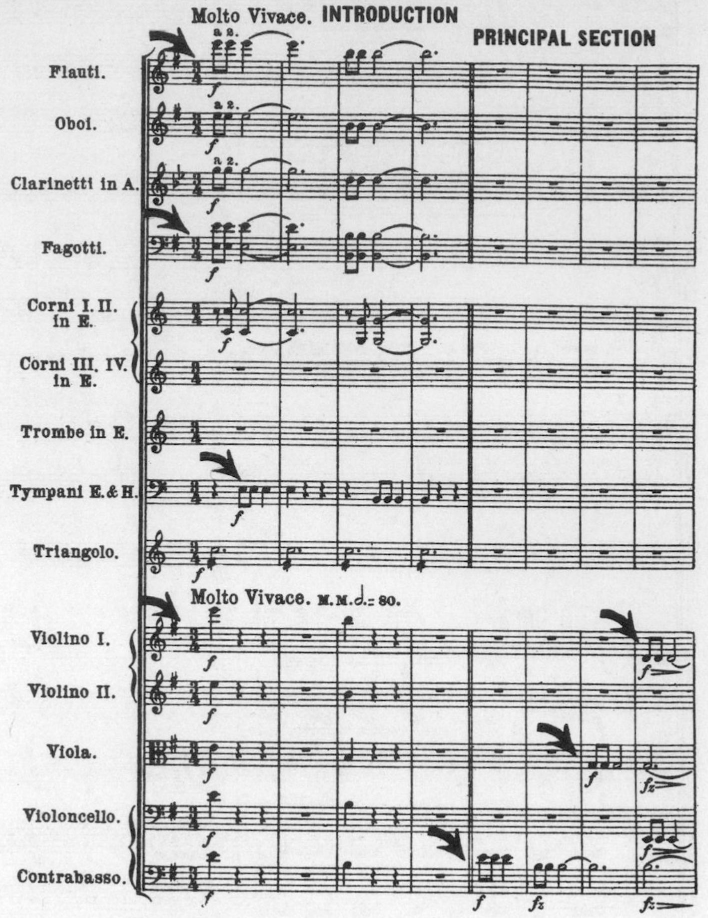

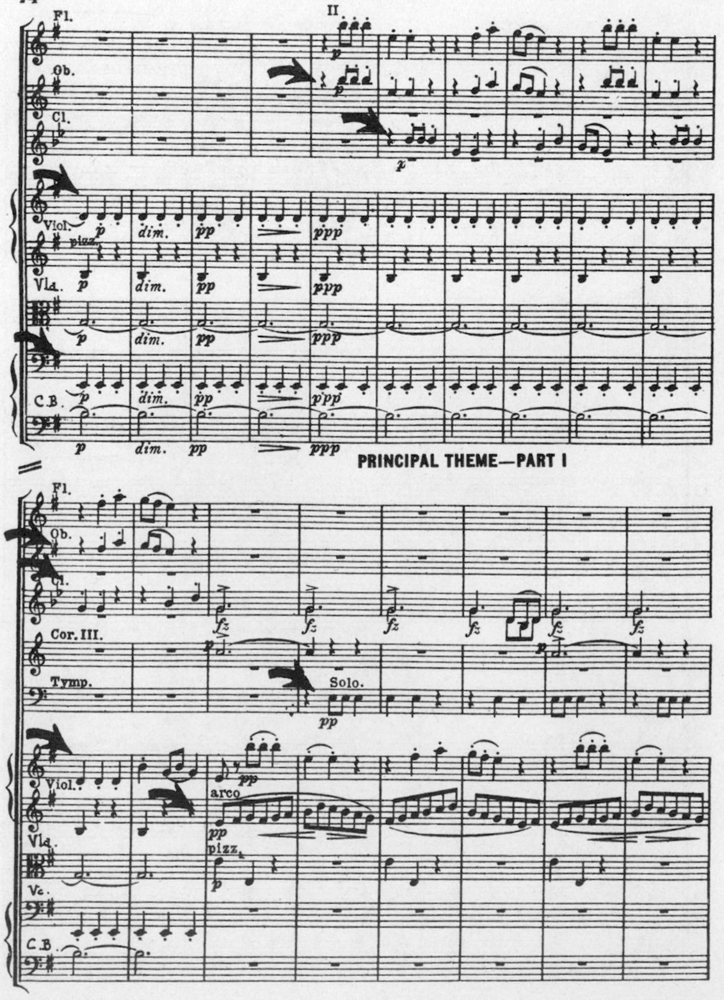

75

Ob.
Tymp.
cresc. molto
Viol.
Vla.
arco
Vc.
C.B.
PRINCIPAL THEME—PART II
Fl.
Ob.
Cl.
Fag.
a 2.
Cor.
Tymp.
Viol.
Vla.
Vc.
C.B.
div.
PRINCIPAL THEME—

76

Fl.
Ob.
Cl.
Fag.
a 2.
Cor.
Tr.
Tym.
Tri.
Viol.
Vla.
Vc.
C.B.
PART III

77

Fl.
Ob.
a 2
Cl.
Fag.
Cor.
Tr.
Tym.
Tri.
Viol.
Vla.
Vc.
C.B.

78

Cl.
Fag.
Viol.
Vla.
Vc.
C.B.
dim.
BRIDGE PASSAGE
TRIO I
Poco sostenuto.
Fl.
Ob.
Cl.
Fag.
Poco sostenuto.
Viol.
Vla.
C.B.
FIRST SUBORDINATE THEME—PART I

79

81

FIRST SUBORDINATE THEME—PART III

80

FIRST SUBORDINATE THEME—PART II

82

RETURNING PASSAGE (RETRANSITION)

83

84

RETURN PRINCIPAL THEME—PART III

85

86

BRIDGE PASSAGE ∿∿∿

TRIO II

SECOND SUBORDINATE THEME—PART I,

1st PERIOD ∿∿∿∿∿∿∿∿ **SECOND SUBORDINATE THEME—**

PART I, 2nd PERIOD ∿∿∿∿∿∿∿∿

91

92

93

SECOND SUBORDINATE THEME—PART III, 1st PERIOD

94

SECOND SUBORDINATE THEME—PART III 2nd PERIOD

CODA—SECTION I

99
Ob.
Cl.
Fag.
a 2.
Cor.
in E.
Tr.
in E. a 2.
Tym.
in E.H.
Tri.
Vla.
Vc.
C.B.
CODA—SECTION 2

101

Fl
Ob.
Cl.
Fag.
Cor.
Tr.
Tym.
Tri.
Viol.
dim.
Vla.
C.B.

100
Fl.
Ob.
Cl.
Fag.
dim.
Cor.
Tr.
Tym.
Tri.
Viol.
Vla.
C.B.

102
Fl.
Ob.
Cl.
Fag.
G. P.
Cor.
Tr.
Tym.
Tri.
pizz.
arco
Viol.
Vla.
Vc.
C.B.

IV.

INTRODUCTION

EXPOSITION

PRINCIPAL THEME—PART I

107

PRINCIPAL THEME—PART II

108

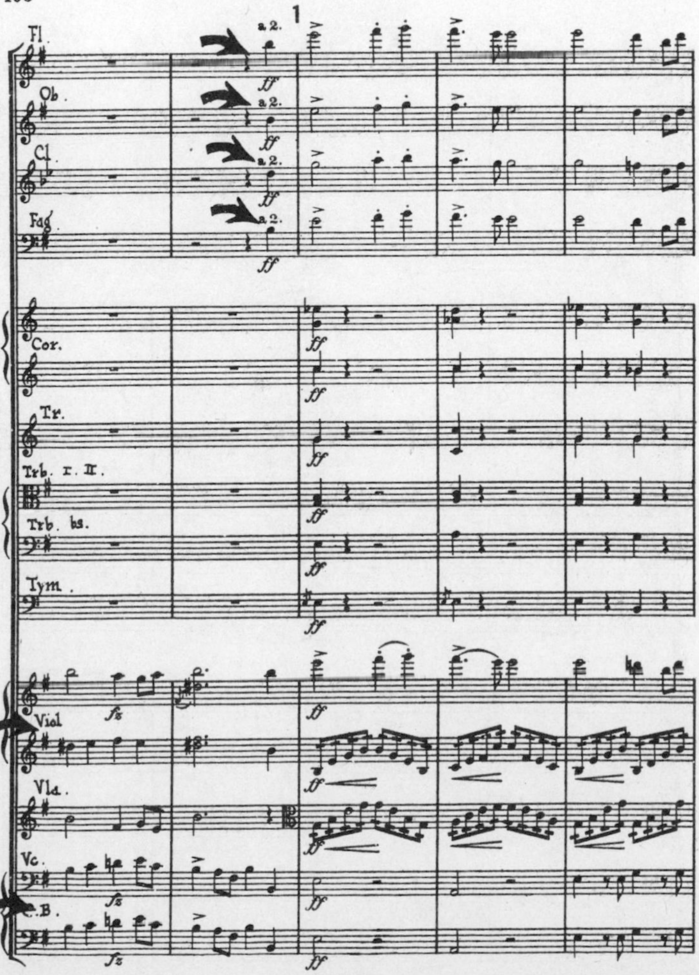

PRINCIPAL THEME—PART III

109

110

BRIDGE PASSAGE—PART I

111

113

BRIDGE PASSAGE—PART III

112

BRIDGE PASSAGE—PART II

114

115

116

SUBORDINATE THEME—PART I

117

SUBORDINATE THEME—PART II

118

SUBORDINATE THEME—PART III

SUBORDINATE THEME—

PART IV

CODETTA—PART I

123
Fl
a 2.
Ob.
Cl.
Fag.
Cor.
Tr.
Trb. I. II.
Trb. bs.
Tym.
Viol.
Vla.
Vc.
C.B.

124
Fl
Ob.
Cl.
Fag.
Cor. III. IV.
sempre diminuendo
Viol.
Vla.
pizz.
arco
Vc.
C.B.
dim.

125
Cl.
a 2.
Fag.
Viol.
Vla.
pizz.
Vc.
C.B.
5
Fl.
Ob.
Tymp.
arco
CODETTA—PART II

126
Fl
Ob.
Cl.
Fag.
in F.
a 2.
Cor.
in E
Tr.
Trb. I. II.
Trb. bs.
Tym.
Viol.
Vla.
Vc.
C.B.
dim.

127

128

129

6 DEVELOPMENT

DEVELOPMENT—SECTION I

130

131
Fl.
Ob.
Fag.
Cor.
Viol.
Vla.
Vc.
C.B.
DEVELOPMENT—SECTION 2
Cl.
Cor. I u. II.
dim.
133
cresc. molto
Tr.
Trb. I. II.
Trb. bs.
Tym.
Muta E in Es.
cresc.
Vcl.
132
7
Cor. III u. IV.
Tymp. in H.
134
in Es.
a 2.
cresc. molto

135

RETURNING PASSAGE (RETRANSITION)

136

137

138

139
Fl.
Ob.
Cl.
Fag.
Cor.
Tr.
Trb. I. II.
Trb. bs.
Tym.
Viol.
Vla.
Vc.
C.B.

141
Fl.
9 Meno mosso.
Ob.
a 2.
dim.
Cl.
pp dim.
Fag.
Cor. a 2.
Tr. a 2.
Trb. I. II.
Trb. bs.
Tym.
Meno mosso.
Viol.
Vla.
Vc.
C.B.
THEME

140
Fl.
Ob.
Cl.
Fag.
Cor.
Tr.
Trb. I. II.
a 2.
Trb. bs.
Tym.
RECAPITULATION
Viol.
Vla.
Vc.
C.B.
RETURN PRINCIPAL

142
Ob.
Cl.
Cor. I u. II.
Tromb. I u. II.
Tromb. basso
Tymp.
in E. H.
Viol.
dim.
Vla.
Vc.
C.B.
in tempo
Solo.
Fag.
molto cresc.
Viol.
Vla.
Vc.
C.B.
pizz.
RETURN SUBORDINATE

143
Fl.
Ob.
Cl.
Fag.
Cor. I u. II.
Viol.
Vla.
Vc.
C.B.
THEME—PART I
dim.

144
Fl.
Ob.
Cl.
Cor. I u. II.
Viol.
Vla.
Vc.
C.B.
a 2.
cresc.
molto
arco
RETURN SUBORDINATE THEME—PART II
Fag.
dim.

145
Fl.
10 Un poco sostenuto
Ob.
Cl.
Fag.
Cor. I u. II.
Tymp.
in E.H.
Un poco sostenuto
Viol.
Vla.
Vc.
C.B.
RETURN SUBORDINATE THEME—PART III

146
Fl.
Ob.
Cl.
Fag.
Solo. marc.
Tymp.
Viol.
div.
Vla.
Vc.
C.B.
a 2.
staccato

147
Fl.
Ob.
Cl.
Fag.
Cor.
Tr.
Trb. I. II.
Trb. bs.
Tym.
Viol.
Vla.
Vc.
C.B.
dim.
pp
ppp

148
Fl.
Ob.
Cl.
Fag.
stringendo
Cor.
Solo.
a 2.
dim.
cresc.
Tr.
Trb. I. II.
Trb. bs.
C.B.
Viol.
Vla.
Vc.
C.B.

149
Tempo I.
CODA
11
Fl.
Ob.
Cl.
Fag.
Cor.
molto cresc.
Tr.
cresc.
in E.
Trb. I. II.
Trb. bs.
Tym.
Tempo I.
Viol.
Vla.
Vc.
C.B.
CODA—SECTION 1
CODA—SECTION 2

150
Fl.
Ob.
Cl.
Fag.
a 2.
Cor.
Tr.
Trb. I. II.
Trb. bs.
Tym.
Viol.
Vla.
Vc.
C.B.

151

153

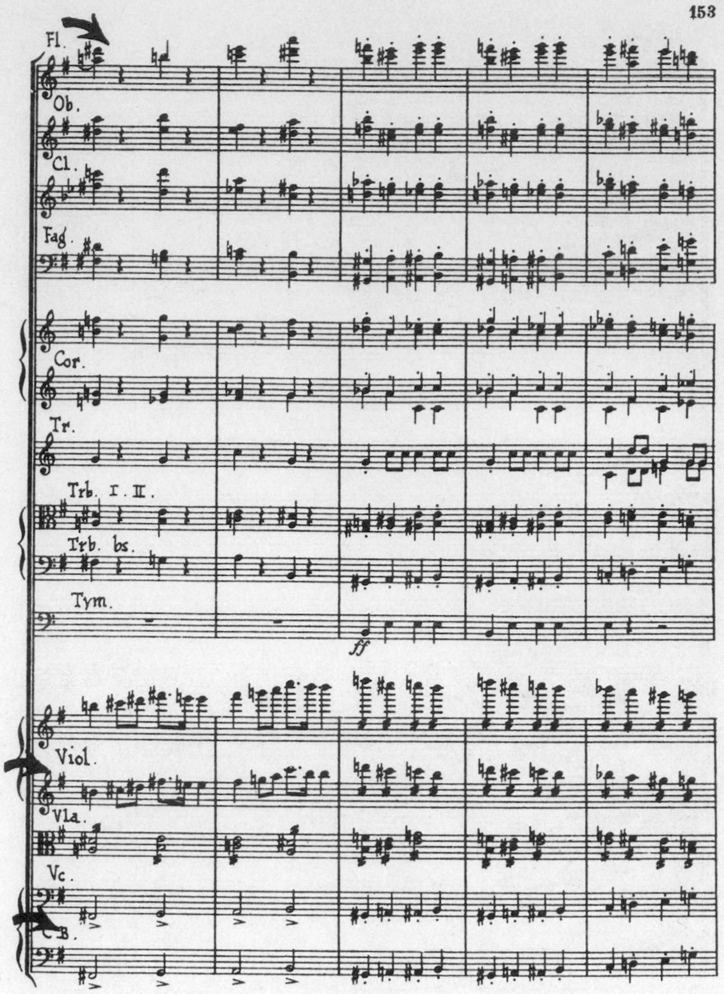

152

CODA—SECTION 3

154

CODA—SECTION 4

155
Fl.
Ob.
Cl.
Fag.
Cor.
Tr.
Trb. I. II.
Trb. bs.
Tym.
Viol.
Vla.
Vc.
C.B.
fz
fff

156
Fl.
Ob.
a 2.
Cl.
Fag.
Cor.
Tr.
Trb. I. II.
Trb. bs.
Tym.
Viol.
Vla.
Vc.
C.B.
dim.
p
sempre più

157
Cl.
Solo.
Fag.
Tymp.
Viol.
Vla.
Vc.
C.B.
dim.
pp
p
CODA—SECTION 5
Fl.
Cl.
legato
ppp
Viol.
Vla.
Vc.
C.B.

158
Fl.
poco a poco rit.
in tempo
Ob.
Cl.
Fag.
Solo.
Cor.
Tr.
Trb. I. II.
Trb. bs.
Tym.
ppp
pp
p
poco a poco rit.
in tempo
Viol.
Vla.
Vc.
C.B.
cresc.
CODA—SECTION 6

159
Meno.
ritard.
in tempo
a 2.
Fl.
Ob.
Cl.
Fag.
Cor.
Tr.
Trb. I. II.
Trb. bs.
Tym.
Viol.
Vla.
Vc.
C.B.
gro con fuoco.)
161
non div.
160
un poco meno mosso.
in tempo (Alle-
div.
162
lunga
dim.
ppp
CODA—SECTION 7

ITALIAN SYMPHONY, Op. 90 *FELIX MENDELSSOHN*

MOVEMENTS:

I. *Allegro vivace*
II. *Andante con moto*
III. *Con moto moderato*
IV. *Presto (Saltarello)*

The Italian Symphony is scored for the following instruments:

2 Flauti (Flutes)	*Fl.*	2 Timpani (Tympani)	*Timp.*
2 Oboi (Oboes)	*Ob.*	1. Violini (1st Violins)	*Viol.*
2 Clarinetti (Clarinets)	*Cl.*	2. Violini (2nd Violins)	*Viol.*
2 Fagotti (Bassoons)	*Fg.*	Violi (Violas)	*Vla.*
2 Corni (Horns)	*Cor.*	Violoncelli (Violoncellos)	*Vc.*
2 Trombe (Trumpets)	*Tbe.*	Contrabassi (Double Basses)	*Cb.*

Each instrument is listed above under its name as printed on the first page of the score; its English equivalent, and the abbreviation used on succeeding pages.

Mendelssohn completed this symphony, according to the autograph date on the score, on March 13, 1883. It was begun during his sojourn in Italy (1830-31), and the brilliant *Saltarello* which forms the last movement was probably inspired by the Carnival at Rome of which he was an interested spectator during February, 1831.

The symphony was first performed by the Philharmonic Society of London on May 13, 1833, and conducted by the composer, who also electrified the audience by a performance of Mozart's Concerto for Piano in D minor. Evidently Mendelssohn was not satisfied with the original scoring of the symphony for he began to revise it in 1834, completing the revision during the latter part of 1837. The new version was first performed at a Gewandhaus concert in Leipzig on November 1, 1849, with Julius Rietz conducting. The reception at both premières was extremely favorable.

Three recordings are available of this symphony: one by the Boston Symphony Orchestra under Serge Koussevitzky, another by the Hallé Orchestra with Hamilton Harty conducting, and a third by the La Scalla Orchestra under the baton of Ettore Panizza.

Symphony Nº 4

("Italian")

Felix Mendelssohn, Op. 90

EXPOSITION

Allegro vivace.

5

6

7

PRINCIPAL THEME—PART III, 1st PERIOD

8

PRINCIPAL THEME—PART III, 2nd PERIOD

9
70
Fl.
Ob.
Cl.
Fg.
Cor.
Tbe.
Timp.
Vl.
Vla.
Vc.
Cb.

11
80
Fl.
Ob.
Cl.
Fg.
Cor.
Tbe.
Timp.
Vl.
Vla.
Vc.
Cb.

10
Fl.
Ob.
Cl.
Fg.
Cor.
Tbe.
Timp.
Vl.
staccato
Vla.
Vc.
Cb.
BRIDGE PASSAGE

12
90
Fl.
Ob.
Cl.
Fg.
Cor.
Tbe.
Timp.
Vl.
staccato
Vla.
Vc.
Cb.

Fl.
Cl.
Vl.
Vla.
Vc.
Cb.
Fg.
100
110
sempre staccato
sempre pp e staccato
pizz.
SUBORDINATE
THEME—PART I, 1st PERIOD

Fl.
Ob.
Cl.
Fg.
Cor.
Tbe
Timp
Vl.
Vla.
Vc.
Cb.
120
SUBORDINATE

Fl.
Ob.
Cl.
Fg.
Cor.
Tbe.
Timp.
Vl.
Vla.
Vc.
Cb.
130
THEME—PART I, 2nd PERIOD

Fl.
Ob.
Cl.
Fg.
Cor.
Tbe
Timp.
Vl.
Vla.
Vc.
Cb.
arco
cresc.
SUBORDINATE THEME—PART II

140
Fl.
Ob.
Cl.
Fg.
Cor.
Tbe.
Timp.
Vl.
Vla.
Vc.
Cb.
SUBORDINATE THEME—PART III

150
Fl.
Ob.
Cl.
SOLO
Fg.
Cor.
Tbe.
Timp.
Vl.
Vla.
Vc.
Cb.
CO –

160
Fl.
Ob.
Cl.
Fg.
Cor.
Tbe.
Timp.
Vl.
Vla.
Vc.
Cb.
pizz.
DETTA — PART I

170
Fl.
Ob.
Cl.
Fg.
Cor.
Tbe.
Timp.
Vl.
Vla.
Vc.
Cb.
arco

21
180
Fl.
Ob.
Cl.
Fg.
Cor.
Tbe.
Timp.
Vl.
Vla.
Vc.
Cb.

22
Fl.
Ob.
Cl.
Fg.
Cor.
Tbe.
Timp.
Vl.
Vla.
Vc.
Cb.
pizz.
CODETTA—PART II

23
Fl.
Ob.
Cl.
Fg.
Cor.
Tbe.
Timp.
Vl.
Vla.
Vc.
Cb.
a 2.
arco

24
Fl.
Ob.
Cl.
Fg.
Cor.
Tbe.
Timp.
Vl.
Vla.
Vc.
Cb.
cresc. - - al - f

DEVELOPMENT

DEVELOPMENT—SECTION 1

DEVELOPMENT—SECTION 2

29

220
Fl.
Ob.
Cl.
Fg.
Cor.
Tbe.
Timp.
Vl.
Vla.
Vc.
Cb.
p

30

Vl.
Vla.
Vc.
Cb.
sempre pp
230
cresc.
240
mf

31

Fl.
Ob.
Cl.
Fg.
Cor.
Tbe.
Timp.
Vl.
Vla.
Vc.
Cb.
f
sf
cresc.
DEVELOPMENT—SECTION 3

32

250
Fl.
Ob.
Cl.
Fg.
Cor.
Tbe.
Timp.
Vl.
Vla.
Vc.
Cb.
f
sf

33

34

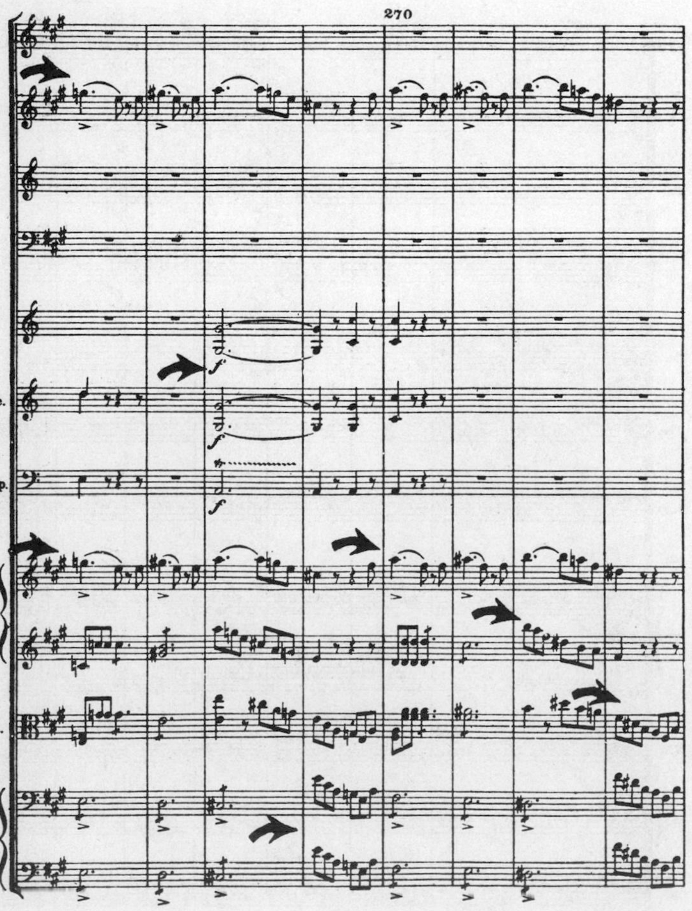

35

DEVELOPMENT—SECTION 4

36

DEVELOPMENT—SECTION 5

DEVELOPMENT—SECTION 6

RETURNING PASSAGE (RETRANSITION)

41

RECAPITULATION

RETURN PRINCIPAL

42

THEME—PART I

43

44

45

47

46

RETURN SUBORDINATE THEME—PART I, 1st PERIOD

48

RETURN SUBORDINATE THEME—PART I, 2nd PERIOD

49

410
Fl.
Ob.
Cl.
Fg.
Cor.
Tbe.
Timp.
Vl.
Vla.
Vc.
Cb.
arco
cresc.
RETURN SUBORDINATE THEME—PART II

51

CODA
480
Fl.
Ob.
Cl.
Fg.
Cor.
Tbe.
Timp.
Vl.
Vla.
Vc.
Cb.
dim.
CODA—SEC—

50

420
Fl.
Ob.
Cl.
Fg.
Cor.
Tbe.
Timp.
Vl.
Vla.
Vc.
dim.
RETURN SUBORDINATE THEME—PART III

52

440
Fl.
Ob.
Cl.
Fg.
Cor.
Tbe.
Timp.
Vl.
Vla.
Vc.
Cb.
TION I

53

Fl.
Ob.
Cl.
Fg.
Cor.
Tbe.
Timp.
Vl.
Vla.
Vc.
Cb.
pp
pp

54

450
Fl.
Ob.
Cl.
Fg.
Cor.
Tbe.
Timp.
Vl.
Vla.
Vc.
Cb.
cresc.
p
p
p

55

Fl.
Ob.
Cl.
Fg.
Cor.
Tbe.
Timp.
Vl.
Vla.
Vc.
Cb.
p
cresc.

56

460
Fl
Ob.
Cl.
Fg.
Cor.
Tbe.
Timp.
Vl.
Vla.
Vc.
Cb.
f
cresc.
ff
CODA—SECTION 2

57
470
Fl.
Ob.
Cl.
Fg.
Cor.
Tbe.
Timp.
Vl.
Vla.
Vc.
Cb.
ff
f

58
480
Più animato poco a poco.
Fl.
Ob.
Cl.
Fg.
Cor.
Tbe.
Timp.
Vl.
Vla.
Vc.
Cb.
ff

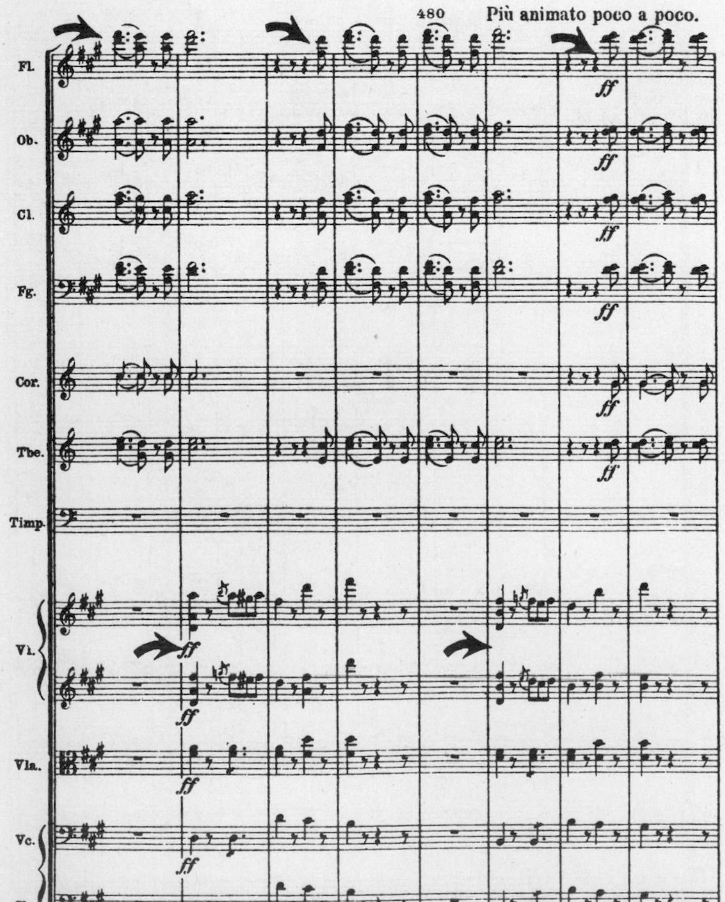
59
490
Fl.
Ob.
Cl.
Fg.
Cor.
Tbe.
Timp.
Vl.
Vla.
Vc.
Cb.
ff
fp dimin. staccato
pe leggiero
p
pizz.
CODA—SEC

60
Fl.
Ob.
Cl
Fg
Cor.
Tbe.
Timp
Vl.
Vla.
Vc.
Cb.
p
f
sempre staccato e p
a2.
TION 3

61

500
Fl.
Ob.
Cl.
Fg.
Cor.
Tbe.
Timp.
Vl.
Vla.
Vc.
Cb.
p
cresc.

62

510
Fl.
Ob.
Cl.
Fg.
Cor.
Tbe.
Timp.
Vl.
Vla.
Vc.
Cb.
cresc.
mf
p
arco
sempre cresc.
sf sempre cresc.

63

520
Fl.
Ob.
Cl.
Fg.
Cor.
Tbe.
Timp.
Vl.
Vla.
Vc.
Cb.
cresc.
f
ff
sf

64

530
Fl.
Ob.
Cl.
Fg.
Cor.
Tbe.
Timp.
Vl.
Vla.
Vc.
Cb.
sf
p
fp

65
Fl.
Ob.
Cl.
Fg.
Cor.
Tbe.
Timp.
Vl.
Vla.
Vc.
Cb.
CODA—SECTION 4

67
550
Fl.
Ob.
Cl.
Fg.
Cor.
Tbe.
Timp.
Vl.
Vla.
Vc.
Cb.
TION 5

66
540
cresc.
a 2.
Fl.
Ob.
Cl.
Fg.
Cor.
Tbe.
Timp.
Vl.
Vla.
Vc.
Cb.
CODA—SEC

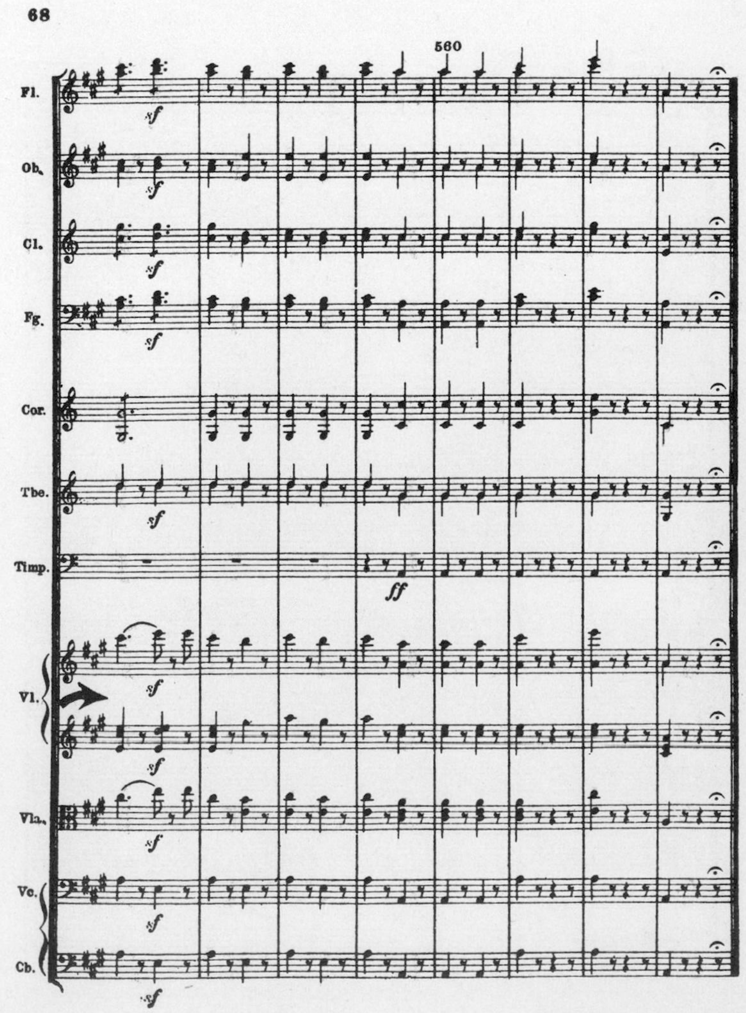
68
560
Fl.
Ob.
Cl.
Fg.
Cor.
Tbe.
Timp.
Vl.
Vla.
Vc.
Cb.

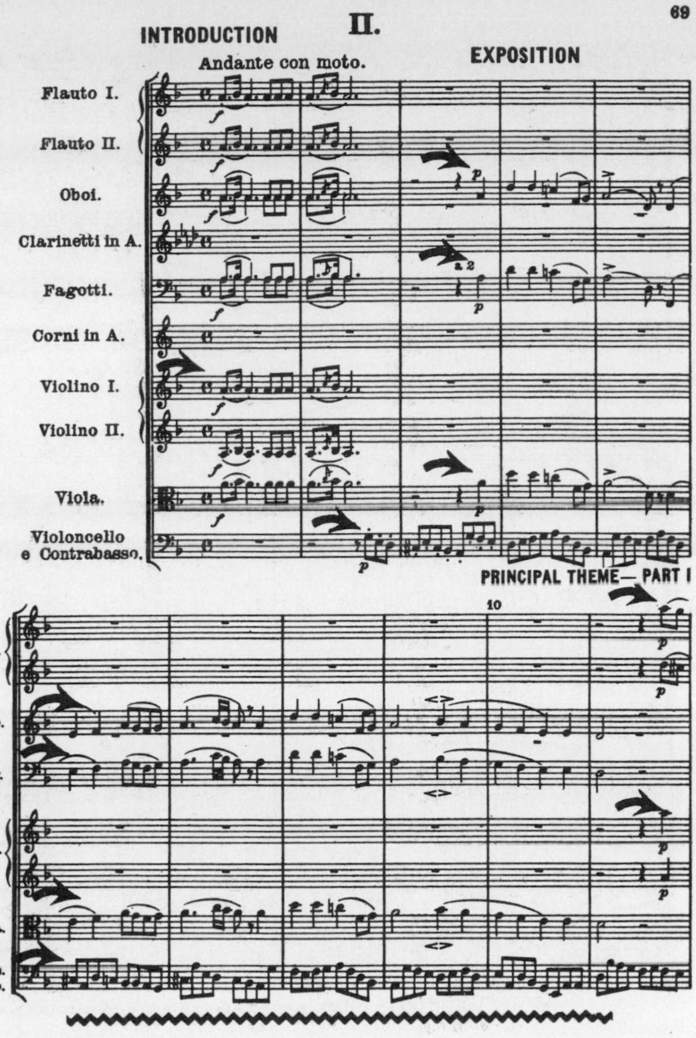

II.

INTRODUCTION

EXPOSITION

Andante con moto.

Flauto I.

Flauto II.

Oboi.

Clarinetti in A.

Fagotti.

Corni in A.

Violino I.

Violino II.

Viola.

Violoncello e Contrabasso.

PRINCIPAL THEME—PART I

Fl.

Ob.

Fg.

Vl.

Vla.

Vc. Cb.

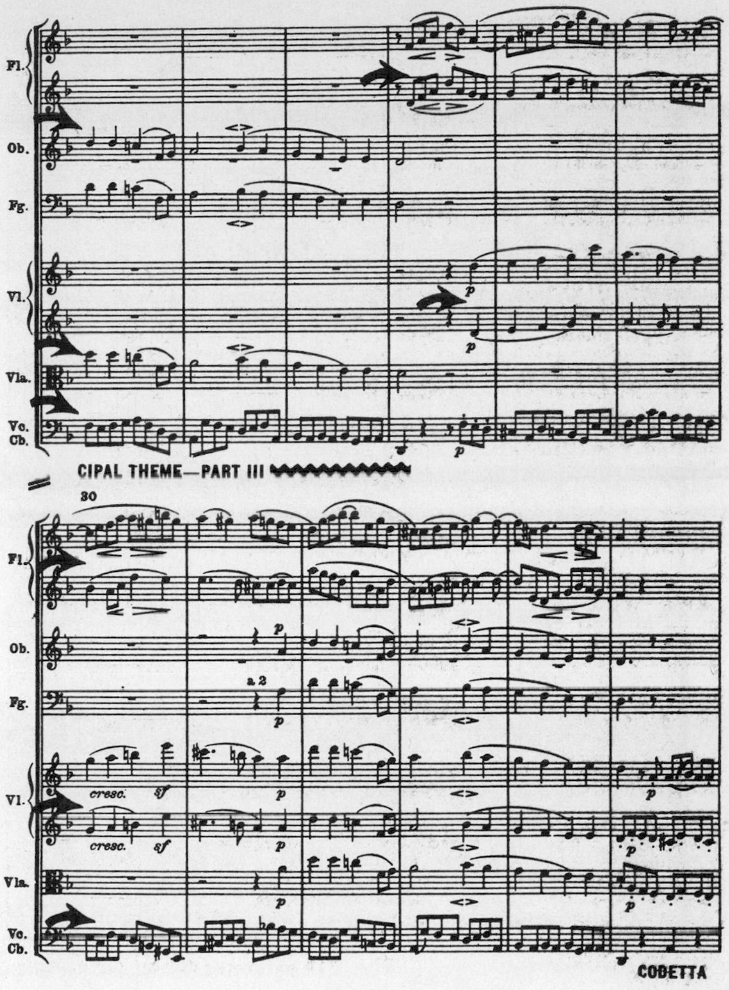

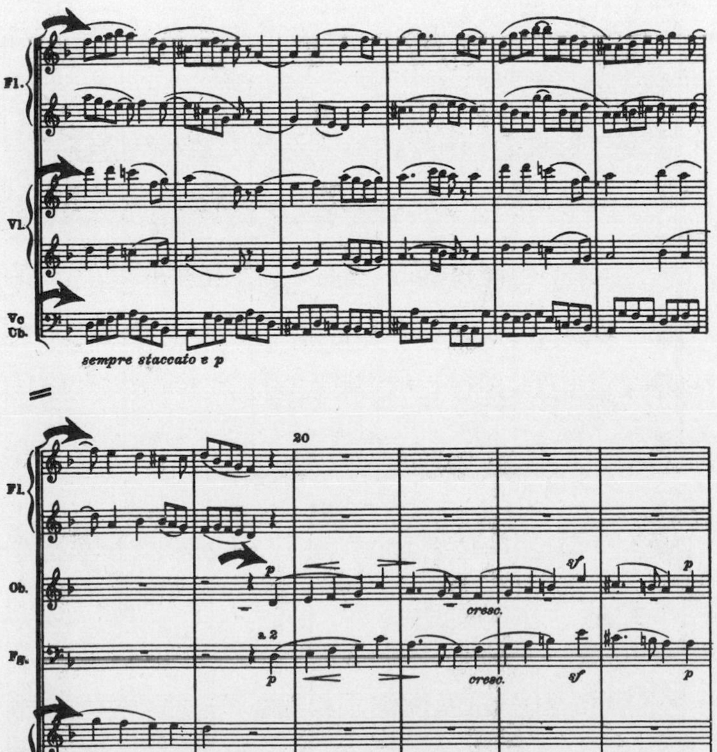

Fl.

Vl.

Vc. Cb.

sempre staccato e p

PRINCIPAL THEME—PART II   PRIN-

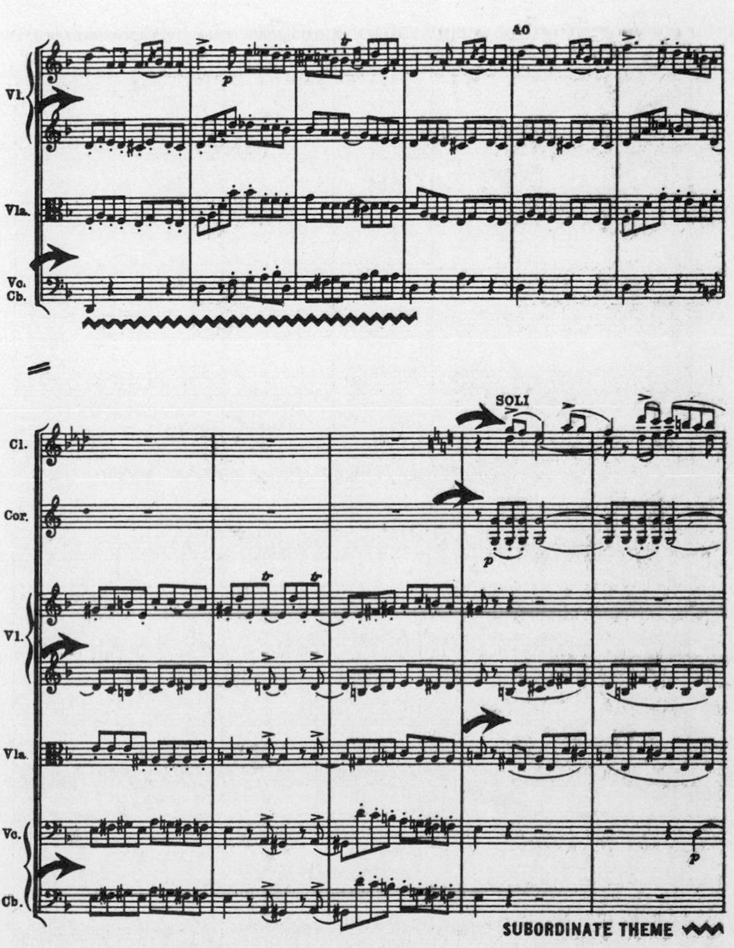

Fl.

Ob.

Fg.

Vl.

Vla.

Vc. Cb.

Fl.

Ob.

Fg.

Vl.

Vla.

Vc. Cb.

CIPAL THEME—PART III

CODETTA

Vl.

Vla.

Vc. Cb.

Cl.

Cor.

Vl.

Vla.

Vc.

Cb.

SOLI

SUBORDINATE THEME

73
50
Fl.
Cl.
Cor.
Vl.
Vla.
Vc.
Cb.
dim.
RETURNING PASSAGE (RETRANSITION)

74
RECAPITULATION
60
Fl.
Ob.
Fg.
Vl.
Vla.
Vc.
Cb.
RETURN PRINCIPAL THEME
sempre p

75
70
Ob.
Fg.
Vl.
Vla.
Vc.
Cb.
dim.
BRIDGE PASSAGE
Fl.
Cl.
Cor.
RETURN SUBORDINATE THEME

76
80
Fl.
Cl.
Cor
Vl.
Vla.
Vc.
Cb.
CODA
dim.
CODA—SECTION I

77

Fl.
Ob.
Fg.
Vl.
Vla.
Vc.
Cb.
a 2
mf
sf
dim.
pp
p
pizz.
Vc. Cb.
CODA—SECTION 2

79

Fl.
Ob.
Cl.
Fg.
Cor.
Tbe.
Timp.
Vl.
Vla.
Vc.
Cb.
p
PRINCIPAL THEME—PART I, 2nd PERIOD

78

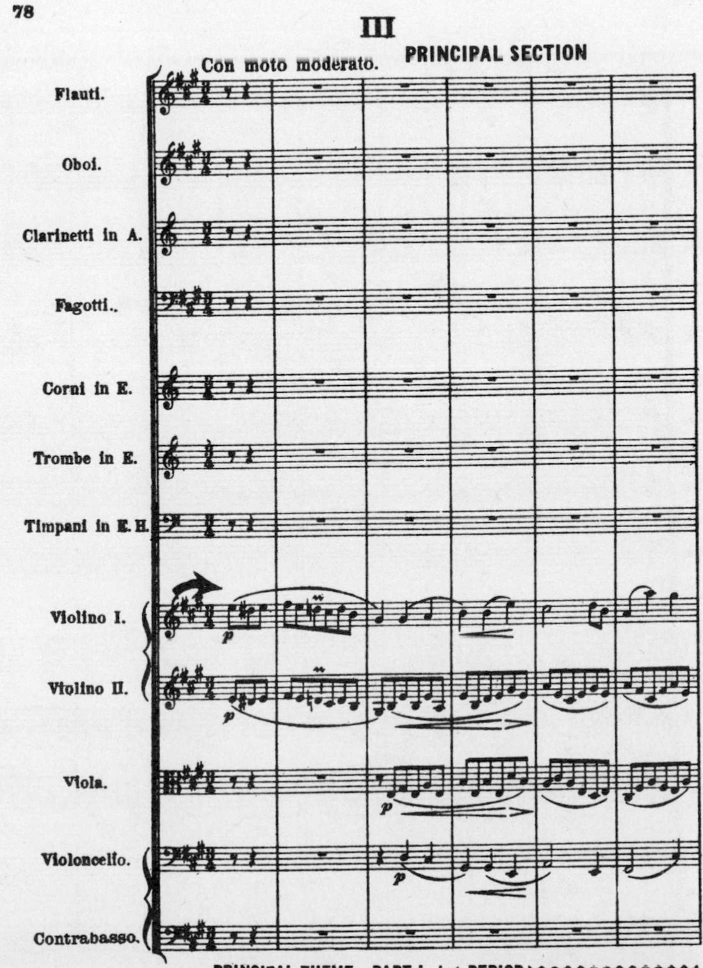
III
PRINCIPAL SECTION
Con moto moderato.
Flauti.
Oboi.
Clarinetti in A.
Fagotti.
Corni in E.
Trombe in E.
Timpani in E. H.
Violino I.
Violino II.
Viola.
Violoncello.
Contrabasso.
p
PRINCIPAL THEME—PART I, 1st PERIOD

80

Fl.
Ob.
Cl.
Fg.
Cor.
Tbe.
Timp.
Vl.
Vla.
Vc.
Cb.
p
CODETTA
PRINCIPAL

81

THEME—PART II

83

PRINCIPAL THEME—PART III

82

84

85

60
Fl.
Ob.
Cl.
Fg.
Cor.
Tbe.
Timp.
Vl.
Vla.
Vc.
Cb.
RETURN CODETTA

86

Fl.
Ob.
Cl.
Fg.
Cor.
Tbe.
Timp.
Vl.
Vla.
Vc.
Cb.

87

70
Fl.
p cresc.
Ob.
Cl.
Fg.
Cor.
Tbe.
Timp.
Vl.
dim.
pizz.
Vla.
Vc.
Cb.

88

80
Fl.
Fg.
SOLI
Cor.
Vl.
SUBORDINATE THEME—PART I
90
cresc.
Tbe.
Timp.
Vla.
arco
Vc.
Cb.
SUBORDINATE THEME—PART II

100
Fl.
Ob.
Cl.
Fg.
Cor.
Tbe.
Timp.
Vl.
Vla.
Vc.
Cb.
cresc.
f

120
Fl.
Fg.
Cor.
Vl.
Vc.
Cb.
cresc.
sf
p
arco
130
Vla.
BRIDGE PASSAGE
RETURN PRINCIPAL SECTION—PART I

110
pp
Fl.
Ob
Cl.
Fg.
p dol.
Cor.
Tbe.
Timp.
Vl.
Vla.
Vc.
Cb.
pizz.
SUBORDINATE THEME—PART III

140
Fl.
Ob.
Cl.
Fg.
Cor.
Tbe.
Timp.
Vl.
Vla.
Vc.
Cb
p
sf
cresc.
RETURN CODETTA
RETURN PRINCIPAL

150
160
Ob.
Vl.
Vla.
Vc.
Cb.
Fl.
Cl.
Fg.
cresc.
dim.
THEME—PART II
RETURN PRINCIPAL

170
Fl.
Ob.
Cl.
Fg.
Cor.
Tbe.
Timp.
Vl.
Vla.
Vc.
Cb.
THEME—PART III

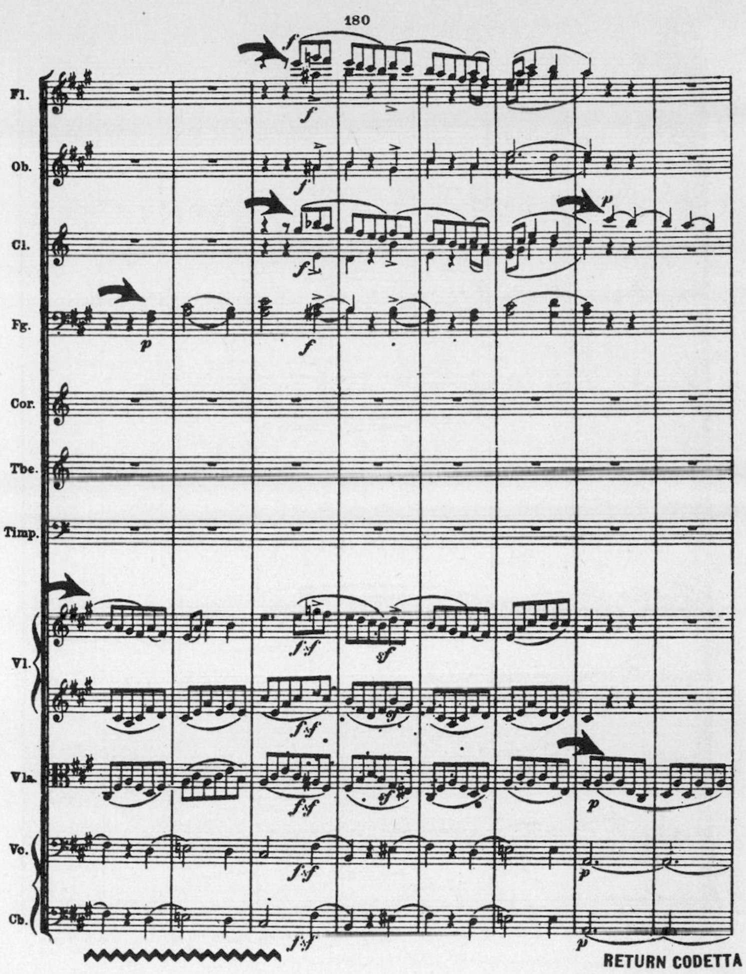
180
Fl.
Ob.
Cl.
Fg.
Cor.
Tbe.
Timp.
Vl.
Vla.
Vc.
Cb.
RETURN CODETTA

190
Fl.
Ob.
Cl.
Fg.
Cor.
Tbe.
Timp.
Vl.
Vla.
Vc.
Cb.

200
Fl.
Ob.
Cl.
Fg.
Cor.
Tbe.
Timp.
Vl.
Vla.
Vc.
Cb.
p cresc.
p
dim.

210
Fl.
Ob.
Cl.
Fg.
Cor.
Tbe.
Timp.
Vl.
Vla.
Vc.
Cb.
p
dim.

CODA
Fl.
Ob.
Cl.
Fg.
Cor.
Tbe.
Timp.
Vl.
Vla.
Vc.
Cb.
pp
p
pizz.
arco

220
Fl.
Ob
Cl.
Fg.
Cor.
Tbe.
Timp.
Vl.
Vla.
Vc.
Cb.
p
pp
dim.
pizz.

IV

Saltarello

Presto.

INTRODUCTION

EXPOSITION

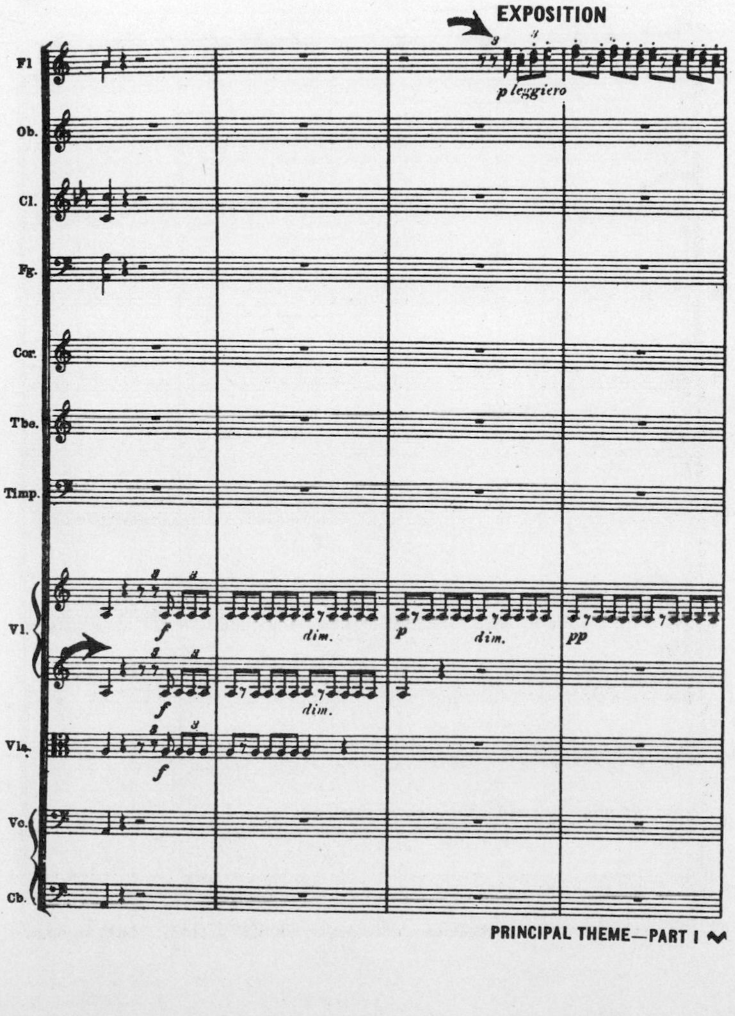

PRINCIPAL THEME—PART I

105

106

PRINCIPAL THEME—PART II

107

108

PRINCIPAL THEME—PART III

Fl.
Ob.
Cl.
Fg.
Cor.
Tbe.
Timp.
Vl.
Vla.
Vc.
Cb.

Fl.
Ob.
Cl.
Fg.
Cor.
Tbe.
Timp.
Vl.
Vla.
Vc.
Cb.

40
Fl.
Ob.
Cl.
Fg.
Cor.
Tbe.
Timp.
Vl.
Vla.
Vc.
Cb.

Fl.
Ob.
Cl.
Fg.
Cor.
Tbe.
Timp.
Vl.
Vla.
Vc.
Cb.

113
50
Fl.
Ob.
Cl.
Fg.
Cor.
Tbe.
Timp.
Vl.
Vla.
Vc.
Cb.
SUBORDINATE THEME

114
Fl.
Ob.
Cl.
Fg.
Cor.
Tbe.
Timp.
Vl.
Vla.
Vc.
Cb.

115
60
Fl.
Ob.
Cl.
Fg.
Cor.
Tbe.
Timp.
Vl.
Vla.
Vc.
Cb.

116
Fl.
Ob.
Cl.
Fg.
Cor.
Tbe.
Timp.
Vl.
Vla.
Vc.
Cb.

117
70
Fl.
Ob.
Cl.
Fg.
Cor.
Tbe.
Timp.
Vl.
Vla.
Vc.
Cb.
sfp
sf
p

118
Fl.
Ob.
Cl.
Fg.
Cor
Tbe.
Timp.
Vl.
Vla.
Vc.
Cb.
p leggiero
stacc.
pizz.
p
CODETTA—PART I

119
80
Fl.
Ob.
Cl.
Fg.
Cor.
Tbe.
Timp.
Vl.
Vla.
Vc.
Cb.
cresc.
p
p cresc.

120
a 2.
Fl.
Ob.
Cl.
Fg.
Cor.
Tbe.
Timp.
Vl.
Vla.
Vc.
Cb.
ff
f
sfff
arco
CODETTA—PART II

121

123

PART III

122

CODETTA-

124

DEVELOPMENT

BRIDGE PASSAGE DEVELOPMENT—

125

SECTION I

126

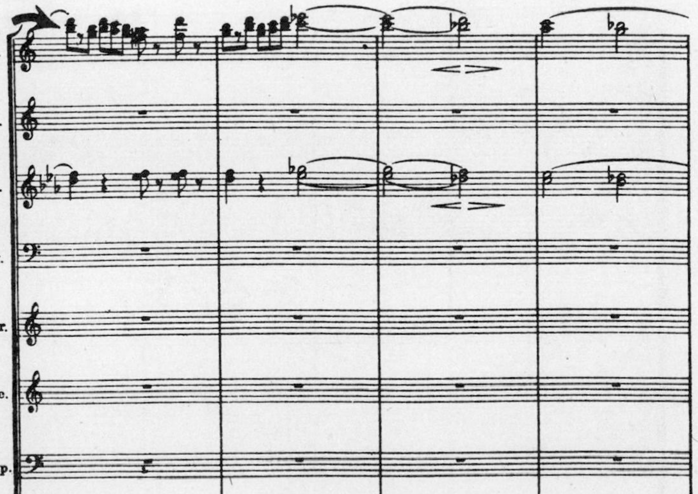

127

128

DEVELOPMENT—SECTION 2

129
Vl.
pp
Vla.
Vc.
Cb.
130
p

131
Fl.
Ob.
Cl.
Fg.
Cor.
Tbe.
Timp.
Vl.
Vla.
Vc.
Cb.
150
p

130
Vl.
Vla.
Vc.
Cb.
140
p sempre
p
Fg.

132
Fl.
Ob.
Cl.
Fg.
Cor.
Tbe.
Timp.
Vl.
Vla.
Vc.
Cb.

Fl.
Ob.
Cl.
Fg.
Cor.
Tbe.
Timp.
Vl.
Vla.
Vc.
Cb.
p

a 2
Fl.
Ob.
Cl.
Fg.
Cor.
Tbe.
Timp.
Vl.
Vla.
Vc.
Cb.
f
cresc.

160
Fl.
Ob.
Cl.
Fg.
Cor.
Tbe.
Timp.
Vl.
Vla.
Vc.
Cb.
cresc.

170
Fl.
Ob.
Cl.
Fg.
Cor.
Tbe.
Timp.
Vl.
Vla.
Vc.
Cb.
f

137

138

DEVEL –

139

OPMENT—SECTION 3

140

CODA
190
Fl.
Ob.
Cl.
Fg.
Cor.
Tbe.
Timp.
Vl.
Vla.
Vc.
Cb.
a 2.
ff
f
CODA—

200
Fl.
Ob.
Cl.
Fg.
Cor.
Tbe.
Timp.
Vl.
Vla.
Vc.
Cb.
p

Fl.
Ob.
Cl.
Fg.
Cor.
Tbe.
Timp.
Vl.
Vla.
Vc.
Cb.
p
dim.
SECTION I

Fl.
Ob.
Cl.
Fg.
Cor.
Tbe.
Timp.
Vl.
Vla.
Vc.
Cb.
p
cresc.

145

146

CODA—SECTION 2

147

148

CODA—SECTION 3

150

CODA—SECTION 4

152

154

SECTION 5

156

SYMPHONY No. 2, Op. 27 *SERGEI RACHMANINOFF*

MOVEMENTS:

I. *Largo-Allegro moderato*

II. *Scherzo-Allegro molto*

III. *Adagio*

IV. *Allegro vivace*

Symphony No. 2 is scored for the following instruments:

1 Flauto Piccolo (Piccolo)	*Fl. Picc.*	3 Timpani (Tympani)	*Timp.*
3 Flauti (Flutes)	*Fl.*	Piatti (Cymbals)	*Piatti*
3 Oboi (Oboes)	*Ob.*	Gran Cassa (Bass Drum)	*Gr. Cassa*
1 Corno inglese (English Horn)	*C. ingl.*	Glockenspiel (Orchestra Bells)	*Glock.*
2 Clarinetti (Clarinets)	*Clar.*	Tamburo (Side Drum)	*Tam.*
1 Clarinetto basso (Bass Clarinet)	*Cl. basso*	1. Violini (1st Violins)	*Viol.*
2 Fagotti (Bassoons)	*Fag.*	2. Violini (2nd Violins)	*Viol.*
4 Corni (Horns)	*Cor.*	Violi (Violas)	*Viole*
3 Trombe (Trumpets)	*Tr.*	Violoncelli (Violoncellos)	*Vcl.*
3 Tromboni (Trombones)	*Trom.*	Bassi (Double Basses)	*Cb.*
1 Tuba (Tuba)	*Tuba*		

Each instrument is listed above under its name as printed on the first page of the score; its English equivalent, and the abbreviation used on succeeding pages.

Rachmaninoff wrote this symphony during an extended visit to Dresden in 1906; it was first performed during the 1908-09 concert season of the Moscow Philharmonic Society. The conductor was Rachmaninoff, and the symphony's première was a sensational success; the work was awarded the Glinka prize which Rachmaninoff had already won with his second piano concerto. The first performance in the United States was by the Philadelphia Orchestra on November 26, 1909, with Rachmaninoff conducting.

An unusual and interesting incident occurred when Arthur Nikisch undertook to conduct this work in Moscow a few weeks after its première. Nikisch, not realizing that the score was a genuinely complicated one, essayed its performance without rehearsal and without even reading the score himself. The result was an interpretation which, if it had been the première of the work, would have perhaps been fatal to its success. It is characteristic of Rachmaninoff that he displayed no resentment; it is equally characteristic of Nikisch that he thoroughly studied the score before giving a magnificent performance at Leipzig with the Gewandhaus Orchestra.

This symphony has been recorded by the Minneapolis Symphony Orchestra under the direction of Eugene Ormandy and by the Cleveland Symphony Orchestra under the baton of Nicholas Sokoloff. Rachmaninoff himself has authorized certain cuts in the symphony which are to be found in the recording by the Minneapolis Orchestra, and are followed in the miniature score presented here.

1

Symphony No. 2

INTRODUCTION I. Sergei Rachmaninoff, Op. 27

SECTION I

3

2

4

5
Poco più mosso.
Fl.
Ob.
C.ingl.
Clar.
Cl. basso.
Fag.
Cor.
Tr.
Tromb. e Tuba.
Timp.
Piatti e Gr. Cassa.
Viol.
Viole
Vcl.
C.B.
SECTION 2

7
rit.
a tempo
Fl.
Ob. I
C.ingl.
Clar.
Cl. basso.
Fag. I.
Fag. II.
Cor.
Tr.
Tromb. e Tuba.
Timp.
Piatti e Gr. Cassa.
Viol.
Viole
Vcl.
C.B.

6
poco a poco cresc.
Fl.
Ob.
C.ingl.
Clar.
Cl. basso.
Fag.
Cor.
Tr.
Tromb. e Tuba.
Timp.
Piatti e Gr. Cassa
Viol.
Viole
Vcl.
C.B.

8
Fl.
Ob.
C.ingl.
Clar.
Cl. basso.
Fag.
Cor.
Tr.
Tromb. e Tuba.
Timp.
Viol.
Viole.
Vcl.
C.B.

9

TRANSITION TO ALLEGRO MOVEMENT

PRINCIPAL THEME—

11

PRINCIPAL THEME—

10

PRINCIPAL THEME—

12

13

Poco a poco più vivo. (♩= 78)
Fl.
Ob.
C. ingl.
Clar.
Cl. basso.
Fag.
Tr.
Tromb. e Tuba.
Timp.
Viol.
Viole
Vcl.
cresc.

14

Fl.
Ob.
C. ingl.
Clar.
Cl. basso
Fag.
Cor.
Tr.
Tromb. e Tuba.
Timp.
Viol.
Viole.
Vcl.
cresc.

15

(♩= 80)
Fl.
Ob.
C. ingl.
Clar.
Cl. basso.
Fag.
Cor.
Tr.
Tromb. e Tuba.
Timp.
Viol.
Viole
Vcl.
C.B.
dim.
leggiero

16

Ob.
Clar.
Cl. basso.
Fag.
Cor. I. II.
Timp.
Viol.
Viole
Vcl.
C.B.
dim.
Solo
p dolce
rit.
Moderato. (♩= 76)
pizz.
div. pizz.
div.
SUBORDINATE THEME
Fl. I. II.
Ob.
Clar.
Fag.
Cor.
marc.
unis.
arco

17

Fl. I. II.
Ob.
Clar.
Fag.
Cor.
Viol.
Viola
Vcl.
C.B.
cresc.
dim.
unis.
arco
pizz.
dolce
legg.
div.

18

Fl.
Ob.
Clar.
Cl. basso
Fag.
Cor.
Tr. I. II.
Tromb. e Tuba
un poco cresc.
Viol.
Viola
Vcl.
C.B.
cresc.
marc.
unis.
arco
div.

19

Fl.
Ob.
Clar.
Cl. Basso
Fag.
Cor.
Tr.
Tromb. e Tuba
dim.
Viol.
Viole
Vcl.
C.B.
unis.

20

Fl. I. II.
Ob.
Clar.
Cl. basso
Fag.
Cor. I. II. III.
Cor.
Viol.
Viole
Vcl.
CB.
unis.
cresc.
dim.
CODETTA
poco a poco calando
Cor. IV.

21

DEVELOPMENT—SECTION I

23

DEVELOPMENT—SECTION 2

22

24

25

DEVELOPMENT—SECTION 3

27

26

28

DEVELOPMENT—SECTION 4

29
Clar.
Fag.
Cor. III. IV.
Viol.
div.
unis
Viole
Vcl.
C.B.
dim.
Clar.
rit.
Cl. basso
poco marc.
Fag.
in F
Cor.
muta in F
Viol.
perdendo
Viole
perdendo
dim.
Vcl.
CB.
rit.

a tempo più mosso (𝅗𝅥 = 66)
Fl.
Ob.
Cl. basso
Fag.
Cor. in F
a 2
poco a poco dim.
Tr.
Tromb. e Tuba
Timp.
ff sforz.
a tempo più mosso (𝅗𝅥 = 66)
Viol.
Viole
Vcl.
ff sforz.
poco a poco dim.
C.B.

30
Meno mosso. (𝅗𝅥 = 56)
rit.
Ob.
C. ingl.
Clar.
Cl. basso.
Fag.
Cor.
senza sord.
Tr.
Tromb. e Tuba.
Timp.
poco cresc.
Viol.
Viola.
Vcl.
unis.
C.B.
arco
div.
unis.
rit.
DEVELOPMENT—SECTION 5

32
poco a poco crescendo e agitato
Ob.
un poco cresc.
C. ingl.
Clar.
Cl. basso.
Fag.
Cor.
Viol. senza sord.
Viole
Vcl.
unis.
C.B.
DEVELOPMENT—SECTION 6
Fl.
Ob.
C. ingl.
Clar.
Fag.
Cor.
Viol.
Viola.
Vcl.
C.B.
cresc.

33

35

34

DEVELOPMENT—SECTION 7

36

37

39

38

40

DEVELOPMENT—SECTION 8

41

43

42

44

RETURNING PASSAGE (RETRANSITION)

45

RECAPITULATION
Moderato. (Come prima.)
RETURN SUBORDINATE THEME

47

46

48

49

Fl.
Ob.
C.ingl.
Clar.
Cl. basso.
Fag.
Cor.
Tr.
Tromb. e Tuba.
Viole
Vcl.
C.B.
f marcato
un poco cresc.
cresc.
div.

51

Meno mosso.
Fl.
Ob.
C.ingl.
Clar.
Cl. basso.
Fag.
Cor.
Tr.
Tromb. e Tuba.
Viole.
Vcl.
C.B.
p dolce
div.
pizz.
Meno mosso.

50

Fl.
Ob.
C.ingl.
Cl. basso.
Fag.
Cor.
Tr.
Tromb. e Tuba.
Viole
Vcl.
C.B.
dim.

52

calando
dolce
Ob.
Clar.
Cl. basso
Fag.
Cor.
Viole
Vcl.
C.B.
unis.
mf dolce
p dolce cresc.
calando
dim.

53

Cl.
Cl. basso
Fag
Cor.
Viol.
Viole
Vc.
C.B.
un poco cresc.
rit.
Ob.
Più mosso (♩=76)
Clar. a 2
Cl. basso
Fag.
Cor.
Timp.
Viol.
Viole
Vcl. pizz.
C.B.
poco a poco cresc.
div.

55

Fl.
Ob.
Clar.
Cl. basso
Fag.
Cor.
Tromb. e Tuba.
Timp.
Viol.
Viole
Vcl.
C.B.

54

Fl.
Ob.
Clar.
Cl. basso
Fag.
Cor.
I. II.
III. IV. a 2
Tr.
sempre marc.
Tromb. e Tuba.
Timp.
Viol.
Viole
Vcl.
C.B.

56

CODA
Fl.
Ob.
Clar.
Cl. basso
Fag.
Cor.
Tr.
Tromb. e Tuba.
Timp.
Viol
Viole
Vcl.
C.B.

57

58

59

60

PRINCIPAL SECTION II.

PRINCIPAL THEME—PART I

61

63

62

PRINCIPAL THEME—PART II

64

PRINCIPAL THEME—PART III

65
Fl.
Ob.
Clar.
Cl. basso
Fag.
Cor.
Tr.
Tromb. e Tuba
Timp.
Glock.
Tam.
Piatti e Gr. Cassa
Viol.
Viola
Vcl.
C.B.
cresc.

66
Fl.
Ob.
Clar.
Cl. basso
Fag.
Cor.
Tr.
Tromb. e Tuba
Timp.
Glock.
Tam.
Piatti e Gr. Cassa
Viol.
Viola
Vcl.
C.B.
dim.
ff sempre marc.
ff pesante
div.
unis.

67
Fl.
Ob.
Clar.
Cl. basso
Fag.
Cor.
Tr.
Tromp. e Tuba
Timp.
Glock.
Tam.
Piatti e Gr. Cassa
Viol.
Viola
Vcl. div.
C.B.
dim.
f ben marc.
unis.
PRINCIPAL

68
Fl.
Ob.
Clar.
Cl. basso
Fag.
Cor.
Tr.
Tromb. e Tuba
Timp.
Glock.
Tam.
Piatti e Gr. Cassa
Viol.
Viole
Vcl.
C.B.
cresc.
dim.
stacc.
f marc.
poco a poco dim.
f pesante
marc.
THEME—PART IV

Moderato.

SUBORDINATE THEME—PART I

SUBORDINATE THEME—PART II

73

75

74

76

RETURN PRINCIPAL THEME—PART IV

77
Fl.
Ob
Clar.
Cl. basso
Fag.
Cor.
Tr.
Trombe Tuba
Timp.
Glock
Tam.
Piatti e Gr. Cassa
Viol
Viole
Vcl.
C.B.
cresc.
ff marc.
f marc.

78
Fl.
Ob.
Clar.
Cl. basso
Fag.
Cor.
Tr.
Tromb. e Tuba
Timp.
Glock.
Tam.
Piatti e Gr. Cassa
Viol.
Viole
Vcl.
C.B.
dim.

79
Ob.
Clar.
Cl. basso
Fag.
Cor.
Viol.
Viola
Vcl.
dim.
stacc.
p stacc.
Ob. I. II.
Clar.
Fag.
Cor. I. II.
Viol.
Viola
Vcl.
C.B.
perdendo
pp
div.

80
Ob. I. II.
Clar.
Cl. basso.
Fag.
Cor. I. II.
Viol.
Vl.
Vcl
C.B
pp stacc.
ppp
dim.
Cl. basso.
Viol.
Viole.
Vcl.
C.B.
div. pizz.

TRIO

Meno mosso. ($\downarrow$ = 104)

SUBORDINATE THEME—PART I

SUBORDINATE THEME—PART II

SUBORDINATE THEME—PART III

85

Fl.
Ob.
Clar.
Fag.
Cor.
Viol.
Viole
Vcl.
C.B.
dim.
Timp.
leggiero

86

Ob.
Clar.
Fag.
Cor.
Tr.
Tamburo
Viol.
Viole
Vcl.
C.B.
stacc.
dim.
più dim.

87

Fl. I. II.
stacc. e leggiero
Ob. I. II.
Clar. I. II. stacc. e leggiero
Fag.
Cor.
Tr.
leggiero
poco cresc.
dim.
Tromb. e Tuba
Timp.
Tamburo
Piatti e Gr. Cassa
Viol.
Viole
Vcl.
C.B.
div.
pizz.
unis.
arco

88

Fl.
Ob.
Clar.
Fag.
Cor.
Tr.
Tromb. e Tuba
Timp.
Tam.
Piatti e Gr. Cassa
Viol.
Viole
Vcl.
C.B.
un poco cresc.
poco cresc.
dim.
div.
unis.

89

Fl.
Ob.
Clar.
Fag.
Cor.
Tr.
Tromb. e Tuba
Timp.
Tam.
Piatti e Gr. Cassa
Viol.
Viole
Vcl.
C.B.
dim.
unis.
stacc.

91

Poco a poco accelerando al tempo I.
Fl.
I. Ob. II. III.
Clar.
Cl. basso
Fag.
Cor.
Tr.
Tromb. e Tuba
Timp.
Glock.
Tam
Piatti e Gr. Cassa.
Viol.
Viole
Vcl.
C.B.
cresc.
marc.

90

Clar. basso
Fag. Solo
Cor.
Tromb. e Tuba
Timp.
Viol.
Viole
Vcl.
C.B.
stacc.
perdend.
arco
dim.
Cl basso
Fag.
f marc.
div. arco
molto marc.
ff molto marc.

92

a 2
Fl. picc.
Ob.
Cl.
Fag.
Cor.
Tr.
Tromb. e Tuba
Timp.
cresc.
Tam.
Piatti e Gr. Cassa
Viol.
Viole
Vcl.
C.B.

RETURN PRINCIPAL SECTION

RETURN PRINCIPAL THEME—PART I

RETURN PRINCIPAL THEME—PART II

RETURN PRINCIPAL THEME—PART III

97

98

99

100 **CODA**

CODA—SECTION I

101

103

102

104

105
I. II.
Ob.
III.
Clar.
Cl. basso.
Fag.
a 2
Cor.
Viol.
Viole
Vcl.
stacc.
più dim.
dim.
p stacc.
Clar.
Fag.
Cor. I. II.
Viol.
Viola
Vcl.
dim.
pp
div.
pizz.

106
Ob. I. II.
Clar.
Fag.
Cor. I. II.
Timp.
Solo
Viol.
Viole
Vcl.
pizz.
unis. pizz.
pp
Meno mosso. (𝅗𝅥 = 80)
accel.
Ob.
Clar.
Fag.
Tr.
Tromb. e Tuba.
Timp.
dim.
Viol.
Viole
Vcl.
C. B.
arco
cresc.
CODA—SECTION 2

107
Tempo I.
Ob.
Clar.
Cor. I. II.
Tr. dim.
Tromb. e Tuba.
Timp.
Solo
dim.
pp
Viol.
Viole
Vcl.
C. B.
arco
pizz.
Cl. basso
Solo
Meno mosso. (𝅗𝅥 = 80)
Cor.
Tromb. e Tuba.
Timp.
Viol.
Viole.
Vcl.
C. B.

108
accel.
Tempo I.
Clar.
Solo
Cl. basso.
Fag.
a 2
dim.
Cor.
Tromb. e Tuba.
Timp.
Viol.
Viole
C. B.
div.
arco
cresc.
pizz.
pp
accel.
CODA—SECTION 3
Clar.
Cl. basso.
Timp.
Viol.
Viole
Vcl.
C. B.
perdendo
dim.
pizz.
ppp

III.

PRINCIPAL THEME—PART I

PRINCIPAL THEME—PART II

PRINCIPAL THEME—PART III

113

115

114

SUBORDINATE THEME—PART I

116

SUBORDINATE THEME—PART III

SUBORDINATE THEME—PART IV

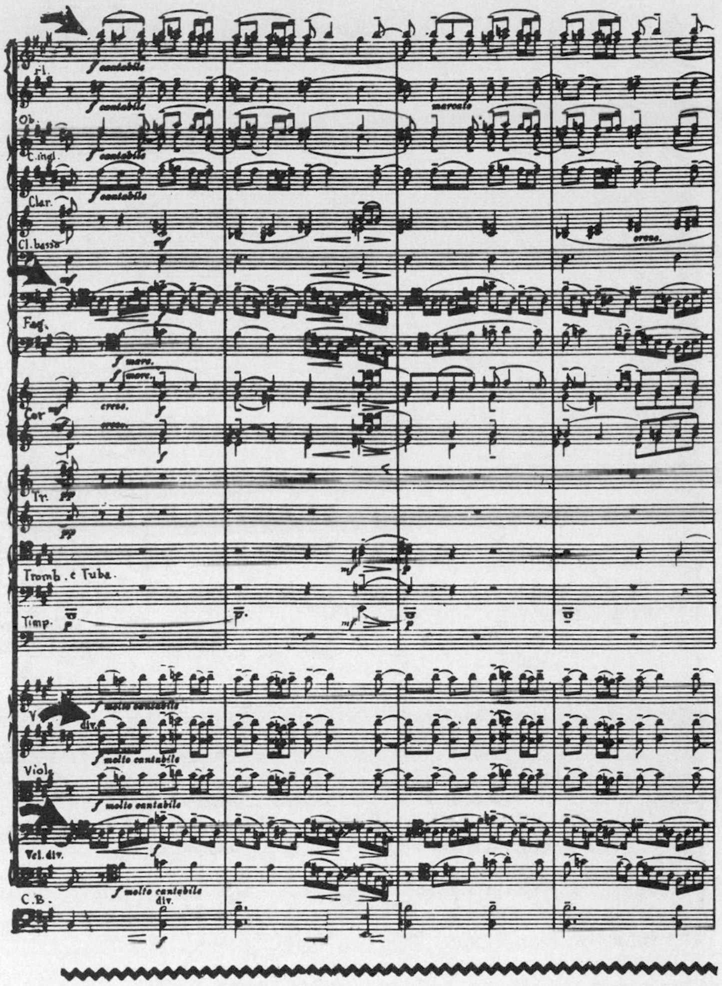

121

122

123

RETURN PRINCIPAL THEME

AND SUBORDINATE THEME (COMBINED)

124

poco a poco cresc.
Ob.
C. ingl.
Clar.
Cl. basso
Fag.
Cor.
Tr.
Tromb. e Tuba.
Timp.
Tutti Viole div.
Vcl.
senza sord.
C.B. unis.
arco
div.
unis.
dim.

I. II.
III.
Ob.
C. ingl.
Clar.
Cl. basso
Fag.
Cor.
cantabile
Tr.
Tromb. e Tuba.
Timp.
Viol.
Viola
Vcl.
unis.
C.B.
cresc.
dim.

poco accelerando
Fl.
Ob.
C. ingl.
Clar.
Cl. basso
Fag.
Cor.
Tr.
Tromb. e Tuba
Timp.
div.
unis.
Vcl.
C.B.
poco accelerando

rallentando
Tempo I.
Fl.
Ob.
C. ingl.
Clar.
Cl. basso
Fag.
Cor.
Tr.
Tromb. e Tuba.
Timp.
Viol.
Viola
pizz.
arco
div. trem.
Vcl.
C.B.
rallentando
Tempo I.

129

Fl. I. II.
Ob.
C. ingl.
Cl.
Cl. basso
Fag.
Cor.
Viol.
Viole
Vcl.
C. B.
Clar.
Cl. basso
Fag.
Cor.
Viol.
Viole
Vcl.
C. B.

130
EXPOSITION IV.
Allegro vivace.
Flauti I. II.
Flauto III e poi Piccolo.
I. II.
3 Oboi.
III.
2 Clarinetti in A.
Clarinetto basso in A.
2 Fagotti.
I. II.
4 Corni in E.
III. IV.
I. II.
3 Trombe in A.
III.
Trombone I. II.
Trombone III e Tuba.
Timpani in Gis. H. Dis.
Glockenspiel.
Piatti e Gran Cassa.
Violino I.
Violino II.
Viola.
Violoncello.
Basso.
PRINCIPAL THEME

131
ff molto marc.
Fl.
Ob.
Clar.
Cl. basso
Fag.
Cor.
Tr.
Trombon Tuba
Timp.
Glock.
Piatti e Gr. Cassa
Viol.
Viola
Vcl.
C. B.

132
Fl.
Ob.
Clar.
Cl. basso
Fag.
Cor.
Tr.
Tromb. e Tuba.
Timp.
Glock.
Piatti e Gr. Cassa
Viol.
Viola
Vcl.
C. B.

Fl.
Ob.
Clar.
Cl. basso
Fag.
Cor.
Tr.
Tromb. e Tuba
Timp
Glock
Piatti Gr. Cassa
Viol.
Viola
Vcl.
C.B.

Fl.
Ob.
Clar.
Cl. basso
Cor.
Tr.
Tromb. e Tuba
Timp.
Glock
Piatti e Gr. Cassa
Viol.
Viola
Vcl.

Fl.
Ob.
Clar.
Cl. basso
Fag.
Cor.
Tr.
Tromb. e Tuba
Timp
Glock
Piatti e Gr. Cassa
Viol.
Viola
Vcl.
C.B.

Fl.
Ob.
Clar.
Cl. basso
Fag.
Cor.
Tr.
Tromb. e Tuba
Timp
Glock
Piatti e Gr. Cassa
Viol.
Viola
Vcl.

137
Ob.
Clar.
Fag.
Cor.
Timp.
Viol.
Viole
Vcl.
dim.
pizz.
Ob. I.
Cl. basso.
Viol.
Viole
Vcl. e Basso.
arco
pp leggiero

138
Ob.
Cl. basso.
Fag.
Cor.
Timp.
Viol.
Viole
Vcl. C.B.
pp
mf
dim.

139
leggiere
Fl.
Ob.
Clar.
Cl. basso
Fag.
Cor.
Tr.
I. II. III.
Tromb. e Tuba.
Tuba.
Timp.
Glockenspiel.
Piatti e Gr. Cassa.
Viol.
Viole
Vcl. div.
unis.
Basso.
cresc.
dim.
più dim.

140
Fl.
Ob.
Clar.
Fag.
Cor.
Tr.
Tromb. e Tuba
Timp.
Glock.
Viol.
Viole
Vcl.
C.B.
cresc.
dim.
a 2
f marcato

141

142

143

144

BRIDGE PASSAGE

145

146

SUBORDINATE THEME—PART I

147

SUBORDI—

148

NATE THEME—PART II

149

150

151

152

Fl.
Ob.
Clar.
Cl. basso
Fag.
Cor.
Tr.
Tromb. e Tuba
Timp.
Glock
Piatti e Gr. Cassa
Viol.
Viole
Vcl.
C.B.

Fl.
Ob.
Clar.
Cl. basso
Fag.
Tr.
Tromb. e Tuba
Timp.
Glock
Piatti e Gr. Cassa
Viol.
Vcl.
C.B.
67

Fl.
Ob.
Clar.
Cl. basso
Fag.
Cor.
Tr.
Tromb. e Tuba
Timp.
Glock
Piatti e Gr. Cassa
Viole
Vcl.
C.B.

Fl.
Ob.
Clar.
Cl. basso
Fag.
Cor.
Viol.
Viole
Vcl.
C.B.
poco a poco dim.
unis.

CODETTA

DEVELOPMENT

DEVELOPMENT—SECTION 1

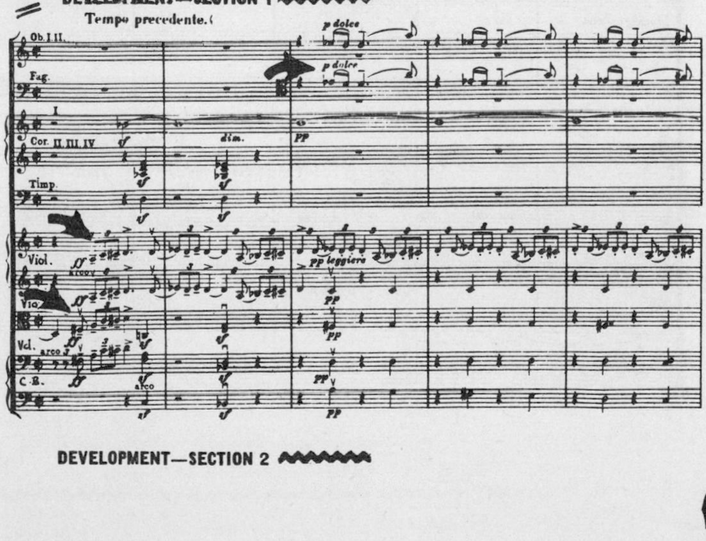

DEVELOPMENT—SECTION 2

161
Fl. I. II.
Solo
Ob. I. II.
Clar.
Cl. basso
Fag.
poco marc.
Cor.
Tr. I. II.
Tromb. e Tuba.
Timp.
Viol.
Viole
p leggiero
Vcl.
C.B
dim.
cresc.

162
Fl.
Ob.
Solo
Clar.
Cl. basso
Fag.
Cor.
Tr.
Tromb. e Tuba
Timp.
Viol.
pp leggiero
Vcl.
C.B.
cresc.
poco marc.
dim.

163
Fl.
Solo
leggiero
Ob.
Clar.
Cl. basso
Fag.
Cor.
Tr.
Tromb. e Tuba.
Timp.
pizz.
f sforzando
Viol.
div.
unis.
Viole
Vcl.
dim. pp

164
Fl.
Ob.
leggiero
Clar.
Cl. basso
Fag.
mf poco marc.
Cor.
Tr.
Tromb. e Tuba
Timp.
arco
Viol.
div.
unis.
p leggiero
pizz.
sforzando
Viole
Vcl.
C.B.

DEVELOPMENT—SECTION 3

RETURN —

ING PASSAGE (RETRANSITION)

169

170 **RECAPITULATION**

RETURN PRINCIPAL THEME

171

172

173

174

175

176

177

Fl.
Ob.
Clar.
Cl. basso
Fag.
Cor.
Viol.
unis.
Viole.
div.
C. B.
cresc.
a 2

178

Fl.
Ob.
Clar.
Cl. basso
Fag.
Cor.
Tr.
Tromb. e Tuba
Timp.
Glock
Piatti e Gr. Cassa
Viol
Viole
Vcl.
unis.
C.B.
div.
dim.

179

Fl.
Ob.
Clar.
Cl. basso
Fag.
Cor.
Tr.
Tromb. e Tuba
Timp.
Piatti e Gr. Cassa
Viole
Vcl.
C.B.
unis.
pizz.
dim.

180

Fl.
Ob.
Clar.
Cl. basso
Fag.
Cor.
Tr.
Tromb. e Tuba
pp poco marcato
poco cresc.
Piatti e Gr. Cassa
Viol
Vcl.
C.B.
cresc.

181

BRIDGE PASSAGE

182

183

184

185

RETURN SUBORDINATE THEME—PART I

186

187

RETURN SUBORDINATE THEME—PART II

188

Fl.
poco a poco cresc.
dim.
Ob.
Clar.
Cl. basso
ff marcato
Fag.
Cor.
II. III. IV.
Tr.
Tromb. e Tuba
Timp.
Piatti e Gr. Cassa
Vl.
Viole
Vcl.
C.B.
unis.
poco a poco cresc.

Fl.
sempre ff e marcato
Ob.
Clar.
Cl. basso
Fag.
cresc.
Cor.
I. II.
III. IV.
sempre ff e marcato
Tr.
ff molto marcato
Tromb. e Tuba
Timp.
Piatti e Gr. Cassa
Vl.
Viole
Vcl.
C.B.
sempre ff

CODA

Più mosso.
Fl.
Ob.
Clar.
Cl. basso
Fag.
ff marc.
Cor.
Tr.
Tromb. e Tuba
Timp.
Piatti e Gr. Cassa
Vl.
div.
unis.
Viole
Vcl.
C.B.
Più mosso.

Fl.
Ob.
Clar.
Cl. basso
Fag.
Cor.
Tr.
Tromb. e Tuba
Timp.
Piatti e Gr. Cassa
Vl.
Viole
Vcl.
C.B.

Ob.
Cl. basso.
Fag.
Cor.
Tr.
Tromb. e Tuba
Timp.
Piatti e Gr. Cassa
unis.

194

a2
Fl.
Ob.
Cl.
Fag.
Cor.
Tr.
Trom. e Tuba
Timp.
Piatti e Gr. Cassa
Viol.
Viole.
Vcl.
C.B.
p
cresc.
sff
ff